THE NEW NATURALIST
A SURVEY OF BRITISH NATURAL HISTORY

GRASS AND GRASSLANDS

The aim of this series is to interest the general reader in the wild life of Britain by recapturing the inquiring spirit of the old naturalists. The Editors believe that the natural pride of the British public in the native fauna and flora, to which must be added concern for their conservation, is best fostered by maintaining a high standard of accuracy combined with clarity of exposition in presenting the results of modern scientific research

Grasses. A watercolour by Dürer 1503

THE NEW NATURALIST

GRASS AND GRASSLANDS

by

IAN MOORE

C.B.E., M.Sc., Ph.D. (Leeds), N.D.A.,
Dip. Ag. Sci. (Cantab)
Principal, Seale Hayne Agricultural College,
Devon
Formerly Professor of Agriculture,
University College of the South-West,
Exeter

WITH 28 PHOTOGRAPHS IN
BLACK-AND-WHITE

COLLINS
ST JAMES'S PLACE, LONDON
1966

© *Ian Moore, 1966*
Printed in Great Britain
Collins Clear-Type Press
London and Glasgow

CONTENTS

PLATES

DIAGRAMS

LIST OF TABLES

EDITORS' PREFACE

The New Naturalist series has already covered many facets of the interrelationship between man and nature, and the Editors are glad to be able to add a further volume of this kind to the series. The grass family has a strong claim to be regarded as the most important to man in the whole plant kingdom, and we are fortunate to have persuaded Professor Ian Moore, the Principal of Seale Hayne Agricultural College in Devonshire, to draw on his unrivalled knowledge of grasses and their utilisation for the writing of the present volume. His special interest is the use of natural and seeded grass pastures for the feeding of livestock. Striking advances have been made in recent years in the improvement of such pastures and Professor Moore has naturally dealt very fully with this vital link in the feeding of the human race; but he also covers that other equally important role of the grass family in our economy, the cultivation of cereal crops for the production of grain. Grass lawns and playing fields form a centre-piece in most British gardens and public parks, and Professor Moore has a chapter on these, but the horticultural value of grasses as ornamental plants in herbaceous borders and woodland gardens is less well known. Professor Moore touches on these and many other unfamiliar uses for the ubiquitous grass family, but grass as fodder is his central theme and his chapters on the historical development of our pastures, their economic significance, and their improvement through the selection and breeding of new strains of wild species make a fascinating story.

Professor Moore does not give detailed descriptions of our 160 or so wild British grasses, as these are easily available in Dr. C. E. Hubbard's excellent Penguin volume, but his keys to the commoner species will enable anyone with a minimum of botanical knowledge to identify these both in flower and from vegetative characters.

Grasses do not lend themselves to coloured illustrations, so we have confined ourselves to a frontispiece of Dürer's superb study, and we hope readers will feel that the fine series of black-and-white photographs adequately represents the family and its contribution to the British landscape.

THE EDITORS

AUTHOR'S PREFACE

Our life is so inextricably interwoven with that of the grasses which grace our fields that the study of grassland is both fascinating and intriguing to all who possess an inquiring mind, be they born and bred in towns or sons of the soil. What is more, the management of the grass sward for farming, sport or pleasure offers a real challenge to skill, in the feeding of plants and the tending of them throughout their life, as well as to one's understanding of technical developments in the realm of botany, chemistry, engineering and economics.

Where should we be without grass? Our life is so dependent on this humble, oft-neglected plant that we must appreciate its real significance in the nation's economy. Without grass our country would lose its scenic beauty, so many sports their colourful background and in scores of ways our lives would be changed. The ordinary grass field one sees every day on any farm, the sports ground with which one is so familiar at school or college or in the wider arena of national games, the small patch of green which graces the front or back of so many English homes, is a complex community of plants each displaying likes and dislikes, and different reactions to varying treatment, yet supplying an essential need whether on the world or simply the individual scale.

For over thirty years my special interest has been grassland and when I was asked by the Editors of the New Naturalist Series to present the story of grassland for their readers, I accepted with alacrity.

In writing such a book one must draw from many sources of knowledge and from many writers of the past and I hope I have made due acknowledgements to the many who have contributed to our understanding of grassland. I am deeply indebted to my own colleagues in College for their ready help and guidance and particularly to Mr. K. C. Vear, Professor H. T. Williams and Mr. R. J. Halley. Not being a botanist, I have had much assistance from Mr. Vear, Head of the Biology Department and as I am not an economist, Professor Williams, formerly Head of Agricultural Economics and now of the University of Aberystwyth, has been of material assistance with Chapter 16; Mr. Halley has given me invaluable assistance with the more practical aspects of grassland husbandry, and Mr. R. W. Younger with Chapter 18. To Mr. D. J. Barnard I am very indebted for help with the proofs.

To the Editors I am grateful for their help in the preliminary stages of writing the book, while to Mr. John Gilmour I am especially indebted for his most valuable criticism and guidance at all stages of preparation. While I hope the book will have a wide appeal generally, I am particularly hopeful that the many schools throughout the country now using a school plot or a school farm or maybe a neighbour's farm as a living medium for teaching, will find it of value. To the many students now attending the recently instituted day-release classes organised by County Education Authorities in agriculture, to those at Farm Institutes and to all students gaining practical experience prior to College or University courses I hope this book will serve as encouragement to a deeper appreciation of the value of the grass crop and an added incentive to further investigation and wider reading.

CHAPTER I

THE ROLE OF GRASS IN NATIONAL LIFE

The significance of grass in the life of man was recognised in earliest times but the distractions of modern life in great cities and the speed with which man now passes through the countryside have caused him to underestimate its importance.

Wherever one travels throughout the British Isles grass is to be seen. Our temperate climate and high rainfall, especially in the western areas, favour the growth of grass which in some parts has a growing season of nine months a year, from March to November. Grassland farming, therefore, is our predominant type of farming, and the efficient production and utilisation of grass are obviously of the greatest economic significance to British agriculture. Agriculture is still Britain's largest single industry and the annual turnover accounts for about 5 per cent of the gross national product thereby exceeding coal (3·2 per cent) and iron and steel (2·8 per cent) which are the next largest industries in gross output. In turn grass, which is our most important crop, makes the greatest single contribution to the farming income. This apart, grass is of prime importance for leisure hours, and our playing fields, which are so much a part of our national life, depend upon grass.

There is obviously a wide range in the types of grassland found in this country, according to the purpose for which they are used. These include bowling greens and cricket pitches with their velvet, close-knit turf, pastures which fatten cattle or carry large herds of milch cows, and moorland sheep walks. Nor must one forget the importance even of the small garden lawn. This may well be the pride of the owner, who mows it with great care each week-end in the summer months. Each type of turf requires specialised treatment and the potential productivity of the different types of farm grassland—permanent meadows, pastures and cultivable leys as well as the rolling hills and moorland which are classified as rough grazings—varies greatly.

Grass provides some two-thirds of the total requirements in terms of starch, and even more in terms of protein, of all the cattle, sheep, and horses in the country. This is shown vividly by the following figures for the area under crops and grass in the United Kingdom in 1961.

TABLE I. AREA UNDER CROPS AND GRASS IN THE UNITED KINGDOM

			acres
Total Crops and Grass			48,820,848
GRASS			
Permanent Grass	12,682,608 ⎫		
Rough Grazings	18,183,421 ⎬		37,868,130
Rotation Grass	7,002,101 ⎭		
CEREALS			7,554,242
Total Gramineae (Members of the grass family)			45,422,372

The astonishing fact is revealed that on 4th June, 1961, when these agricultural returns were made, some nine-tenths of our farmland was under grass of one sort or another, i.e. members of the family Gramineae.

Grass is not, in the great majority of cases, a natural clothing for the earth's surface, provided by a beneficent nature. It is a community of widely differing species and varieties of plants living together in a constant struggle one with another and overshadowed always by the threat of being overwhelmed by weeds, rushes, bracken, heather, gorse, thorns, alder and other trees until, if man allows this process to go unchecked, scrub or even forest reigns supreme once more. Even the patch of lawn is subjected to the same forces and only by constant attention is a weed-free, close-knit, verdant green turf maintained.

During the lean times of farming in the 1920's and 30's, thousands of acres of farm land reverted to derelict grass and scrub, the farmers being forced to save labour, cut out expensive arable crops, and be satisfied with mere subsistence standards of life, since following the first world war the prices obtained for many farm products were less than the cost of production. Then too, in those days cheap imported cattle cakes and food were readily available, which could serve as a substitute for the grass normally fed to stock, not only during the winter months but even in summer. It was by no means uncommon for dairy herds in industrial areas, such as those in Lancashire and the West Riding of Yorkshire, for instance, to be fed wholly on imported feeding stuffs. In extreme cases the cows probably never left the byre, except perhaps to take exercise in a nearby field during the summer months. Under these conditions the productivity of the grassland was negligible and mineral deficiencies in the soil determined that the land was little more than exercise ground.

Grass is a crop requiring the same care and attention as wheat, potatoes, or sugar beet. It needs cultivating, fertilising, and utilising to best advantage and when it receives this treatment the returns per acre can be as high as from any other crop. Moreover, it has a valuable function in restoring fertility to the soil. In two world wars, by plough-ing up a large proportion of our grassland and cropping with cereals, good crops were produced with the minimum of fertiliser, valuable shipping space was saved and a decisive contribution to victory was made.

Mention has been made of the fertility-restoring power of grass and one may rightly ask how this is brought about. The very serious problems of erosion which concern authorities in various parts of the world serve to highlight this vital question of soil conservation. Soil fertility is dependent upon good tilth, maximal water and air, and maximal plant nutrients. Tilth represents the physical condition of the soil in relation to plant growth and each crop has its own require-ments for a seed bed. Ploughing, rotovating, cultivating, disc harrow-ing, and the use of rollers and spiked harrows disturb the soil so that it becomes granular in structure and suitable for the reception of small seeds, yet capable of resisting the shattering and erosive effects of heavy rain until such time as the crop itself provides a close canopy which protects the soil and prevents the fine particles from being washed away by flood waters.

The soil needs to have what is termed "structure." The extremes are sand, which is devoid of structure, on the one hand, and clay, in which the particles are so small that pore space for air and water is virtually non-existent, on the other. Between these extremes lies a "crumb structure" with aggregated particles usually greater than 0·5 mm. in diameter and preferably from 1 to 55 mm. in diameter. When this crumb structure is attained the soil has the capacity to hold enough moisture for the needs of the crop and can resist both "drying-out" during periods of drought and the mechanical stresses of farm equip-ment. Flora and fauna play their part in achieving this ideal through the medium of microbiological activity in the decomposition of organic matter and in fixing atmospheric nitrogen through the medium of leguminous plants. Grassland swards have a vital role to play in the maintenance of fertility since they contain legumes in most cases and when ploughed provide necessary organic matter.

Sandy soils have the advantage of free drainage, good aeration and ease of cultivation, as any gardener on a sandy soil will admit. But these are often too loose and too open in texture and lack the capacity to absorb and hold water and plant nutrients. They are termed "hungry" soils and the limitations of such soils are best overcome by grasses, the fine roots of which physically bind together the mineral particles. Farmyard manure, and green crops which are ploughed in—"green manuring"—perform the same function but a good deal less effectively and at considerably higher cost to the farmer or gardener. Moreover, a long ley or permanent grass sward gives complete coverage from storm water and thus prevents erosion.

Clay soils are very finely-textured and retain moisture to such an extent that a field may be unworkable for several months in the year. Clay is a colloid and therefore very cohesive and highly plastic. Thus when clay soils are cultivated in too wet a condition they become even stickier and are said in farming terms to "poach." Poached land dries out into hard, intractable clods which defy all the efforts of man and machine to break them down to produce a seed bed. In this case granulation of the clay particles to form aggregates—"flocculation" to the chemist—must be brought about, and here again grasses and deep-rooting clovers have a vital role to perform. Farmyard manure, though more effective with clay than with sandy soils, does not increase soil permeability to the same extent as do the fibrous roots of grasses.

I hope I have stressed adequately this unseen function of our grassland. Most people understand the milk or meat-producing relationship between our grassland and the needs of man. Very few appreciate how essential the grass plant is to the whole cropping system of the country.

Grass provides the cheapest way of feeding herbivorous animals during its growing season, while grass conserved as silage or hay, or dried by artificial means, can be used for feeding during the winter months. The following table compares the cost of each food unit ("starch equivalent") from various forms of grass with other succulent foods and clearly underlines the vital necessity of having an adequate supply of fresh grass for feeding.

TABLE 2. COST OF STARCH EQUIVALENTS

Crop	*Cost per ton of starch equivalent*
Grazings	£11·0
Grass Silage	17·2
Hay	19·7
Kale	16·9
Barley	21·3
Oats	30·2
Arable Silage	34·0
Dairy Cake (at £35 per ton)	53·8

Recent research work both in the United States and on farms in this country points to the fact that it may be cheaper and more efficient to mow the grass during the summer months and cart it to the cows, which remain in covered yards—a practice known as "zero grazing," "green soiling" or "mechanical grazing"—rather than to allow the cattle to graze. We shall deal with this question later on.

What are the products of grass? It contributes some 67 per cent of the total feed requirements of all our livestock and since pigs only account for about 3 per cent and poultry 6 per cent, it means that grass provides on the average at least 70 per cent of the diet of cattle and sheep and the few goats. Home-produced veal, beef, mutton, and lamb, our leather and wool, our milk, butter, and cheese, are largely the final product of grass. Few realise the magnitude of these products and their importance to the economy of the country. The table below gives some idea:

TABLE 3. THE GROSS OUTPUT FROM ANIMALS MAINLY DEPENDENT UPON GRASS—UNITED KINGDOM 1961-2

		Value £Million	*Quantity*
Cattle:	Beef	227·1	870 thousand tons
	Veal	5·6	21
Sheep:	Mutton & Lamb	88·7	264
	Wool	17·1	39
Milk and Milk Products		364·8	2388 million gallons
		703·3	

If grass contributes 70 per cent of the total feed requirements of the above stock groups, £492,300,000 of production can be attributed to grassland. This figure represents 31 per cent of the £1,592,000,000 output from national agriculture in 1961-2.

We are all eaters and users of grass. Numbered within the great grass family Gramineae are the cereals—wheat, barley, oats, rye, maize, rice, millet, and sorghum—which provide many of our staple foods. Most of the world's really fertile grassland areas grow cereals so well when ploughed that they are known as "bread baskets." In this category fall the wide prairies of the United States and Canada, the vast grain belts of the Ukraine and Australia, and the pampas of Argentina. Cane sugar is derived from a grass (*Saccharum officinale*). Those giants amongst the grasses, the bamboos, include majestic trees towering to a height of a hundred and twenty feet and some three feet in circumference, forming impenetrable forests as well as providing a variety of useful articles from musical pipes to furniture and domestic utensils. Some grasses are necessary to bind sand and combat the encroaching sea which at certain points along our coastline is ever striving to engulf more and more land. Other grasses provide fragrant oils and perfumes. Lemon grass or Indian grass (*Cymbopogon citratus*), which grows wild in India, is also cultivated both there and in Ceylon and is used for infusing a tea which is reputed to have medicinal properties. *Andropogon nardus* is cultivated in Ceylon and Singapore for the production of citronella oil which is used extensively in the manufacture of soaps and perfumes as well as for the treatment of rheumatism in India. Finally, still other grasses provide the turf we use for sport and recreation.

CHAPTER 2

THE ORIGIN AND DEVELOPMENT OF GRASSLAND

For many generations the term "grasses" as used by farmers had an all-embracing significance and included companion plants like clovers, yarrow, dandelion, ribgrass, and so on, the blending of which made up the turf or sward of a pasture or a meadow which was eaten by horses, sheep and cattle. The term "pasture" usually refers to grassland grazed by animals, while "meadows" are mown for hay. These terms are often used loosely and frequently synonymously, for grassland may be grazed and mown in the same year. Moreover, grazing land is commonly referred to as "meadow" when it borders a stream or river, and in all probability in days gone by it was our poets who contributed to this confusion of terminology. Only in recent years have farmers consciously distinguished between the various plant species composing a particular type of grassland and realised the significance of the grazing animal or the mowing machine in determining the botanical composition of a particular sward or piece of turf. The groundsman, unlike the farmer, abhors all plants other than the special grasses required to produce a hard-wearing turf. Thus the clovers and other miscellaneous plants commonly seen in farm swards and indeed encouraged to flourish there, are eliminated as speedily as possible by both mechanical and chemical agencies when found in the domestic lawn, the cricket field or the golf green.

The history of our grasses from the Ice Age can be traced through the pollen grains which have remained preserved for thousands of years in peat bogs. The pollen of many plants, including the bulk of our forest trees, is liberated in vast showers of golden dust, and is windborne for considerable distances. Even the centres of large cities receive their quota as the sufferers from hay fever know to their cost. Each pollen grain is protected by a thin skin which is highly resistant to decay; consequently when down the ages millions upon millions of these grains have settled on the land and been covered by further deposits they have not disintegrated. It is possible in the laboratory

7

to separate the pollen grains from soil particles obtained by the simple process of boring into ancient lake beds and peat bogs. These can be identified and in this way precise records of the local vegetation can be secured from the glacial period onwards. Such information can then be cross-checked with any geological and archaeological data available enabling a complete picture to be built up.

With the improvement in climate after the final retreat of the ice, the country was covered with vast woods of pine and birch, the only grassland being in parts of the forest cleared by early man. Then elm, oak, and hazel scrub gradually became established as conditions improved.

What of the livestock whose development is intimately interwoven with that of the grasses? Animals clearly related to our present-day grazing animals appear in the fossil records early in the Eocene period, some seventy million years ago. Judging by the structure and arrangement of their teeth, these early ungulates were, however, mainly browsing animals, feeding by cropping the leaves of forest trees. This seems to have been true throughout the Eocene and the succeeding Oligocene period, but at the opening of the Miocene, some forty million years later, there appears to have been a decrease in rainfall and a consequent diminution of forest cover, leaving grasses and other low-growing plants in possession of the plains, both in the Old and the New World. True grazing animals, closely related to modern types, then developed. Antelopes and sheep are recognisable from the Upper Miocene, and oxen, goats, and horses from the following Pliocene period.

The pastures which supplied the needs of the stock of primitive man were as can be imagined but a pale shadow of the excellent swards of to-day. It is unlikely that they did more than keep mature cattle alive, although for a short period during the summer months the best milk cows might have produced a few pints of milk per day, compared to the four, five or six gallons expected now. Nor was the farmer of those times conversant with the needs of the soil, and the constant leaching of nutrients by rain water and the removal of minerals by the stock themselves in the herbage consumed meant that phosphate, lime and potash deficiencies were common. As the fertility of the cultivated ground fell to the point where the yield of grain no longer rewarded the efforts of cultivation, this ground was abandoned. The former arable was then allowed to revert to some form of grass again. Such conditions favour the growth of mat grass (*Nardus stricta*), purple moor grass (*Molinia caerulea*) sheep's fescue (*Festuca ovina*), bent (*Agrostis* spp.), bromes (*Bromus* spp.) and the oat grasses (*Arrhena-therum*, *Trisetum* and *Helictotrichon*), grasses of poor feeding value. These are in marked contrast to the broad-leaved succulent grasses of high feeding value which comprise a good pasture. Farm stock in those early times was small and stunted as shown by the skeletons which have been found and this was only to be expected under such conditions.

The conversion from forest to pasture can be seen in minature on the broad verge of many a farm road crossing or common. Nearest the road, the constant trampling back and forth of cattle, sheep, and horses promotes the growth of the best pasture grasses, such as the ryegrasses (*Lolium* spp.) and the meadow grasses (*Poa* spp.) with wild white clover (*Trifolium repens*) and probably bird's foot trefoil (*Lotus corniculatus*). As the trampling and grazing become less intensive further from the road-side so the bents (*Agrostis* spp.) the fescues (*Festuca* spp.) and Yorkshire fog (*Holcus lanatus*) become more dominant and these in turn are replaced by coarser grasses, the tall fescues, tussock grass (*Deschampsia caespitosa*) and oat grasses until bramble, hazel, blackthorn, wild rose, and hawthorn dominate the scene. It is then only a short step to true forest. This gradual progression from good grass to forest follows any change which results in less intensive grazing or neglect. Should a field be ranched, allowing only a few head of stock on a large acreage of grassland, as opposed to close grazing where many stock are concentrated in a field, or more especially if grassland is allowed to become derelict, young saplings of forest trees spring up and the once valuable turf soon becomes colonised by coarse grasses and scrubby growths reverting back in time to the original forest from which the pasture had been won by the efforts of man.

Not until about 50 B.C. was the liming and marling of fields practised by the Belgae as a means of replenishing the fertility of the soil, and it was very much later that the droppings of animals were collected to be spread as farmyard manure. We owe much to the Belgae; with the eight-ox plough which they introduced, cultivation on a much bigger scale became possible and, moreover, they affected considerable forest clearance with their implements. So successful were their efforts, indeed, that corn and cattle were exported to the Continent, and when Caesar invaded Britain he was able to supply the food needs of his troops from the soil of Kent.

The Romans did little for the grassland of Britain, but after they had withdrawn, the Anglo-Saxon invaders, with great vigour, began clearing more forest land and converting lowland soils into meadows and cornfields. Many more were enclosed for better cropping and compact villages were created. These were usually surrounded by large open fields in which each settler had a number of scattered strips, some for cultivation and others to be mown for hay, the underlying principle being to divide up as evenly as possible the different types of soil with their varying levels of fertility. After harvest the arable and the meadow land were opened for common grazing, the stock feeding on the straw which was left on the arable ground, together with any growth of grass which had been made since the hay was carted. The Anglo-Saxons were really the first farmers to appreciate the need for adequate pasture during the grazing season and the necessity of safe-guarding their stock in winter time with a good supply of hay. By so doing, the former practice of slaughtering in the autumn all the stock which could not fend for itself during the winter was avoided. Each occupier of thirty acres was given at the beginning of his tenancy a cow, two oxen, and six sheep by the lord of the manor and there were no farmers who merely rented the land as they do now. It was possible to increase the acreage of pasture by paying money rent to the lord or by rendering services in the form of additional ploughing. The Anglo-Saxon period was fruitful for Britain, and central and eastern England was dotted with villages which were later recorded in Domesday Book. It was a period of winning from the forest, of settle-ment, and of organised farming.

Domesday Book includes a remarkably comprehensive survey of the land initiated by King William to ensure accurate assessment and punctual payment of tax. The prosperity of each manor depended upon the amount of land which could be ploughed; in essence, upon the strength of its oxen. Plough-teams were in their turn dependent upon an adequate supply of meadow hay for the winter and so large fertile meadows were the key to the farming economy of those days. This is seen in the relative value per acre of meadow land compared with arable, the former often being worth four times as much as the latter. The value of enclosed pasture was usually less than that of meadow land, while the common pasture land in many instances surrounded the village and gradually merged into scrub and woodland which served as a line of demarcation between neighbouring villages. The scarcity of good pasture is a constant theme of all manorial documents of the period.

Reclamation was continued until around A.D. 1500. The twelfth and thirteenth centuries were the period of greatest colonising activity in England, but this colonisation drive was largely over by about

A.D. 1300. Pressure of population seems to have kept peasant demand for land at a high level up to the Black Death in A.D. 1349 although there was considerable contraction of the arable, and hence an increase in grassland, on many estates before A.D. 1300 or very soon afterwards. The Black Death resulted in the death of large numbers of labourers and hence wages rose and the landlords were unable to get their fields cultivated and in spite of legislative measures to resolve the problem a good deal of land simply reverted to grass. This contraction of the arable acreage continued through the late fourteenth century and the first half of the fifteenth. With the break-up of the manorial system a gradual consolidation of holdings took place mainly by exchange. Then too, the trend from a two field system of farming—one field under crop while one lay fallow—towards a three-course system of two fields under crop and one fallow became evident. Ultimately this system gave way to the four course system whereby grass appeared in the open fields which had hitherto been exclusively arable.

The Tudor period was marked by a spate of writings from farmers and historians, and such names as Fitzherbert, Tusser, Leland, Camden and Morden are an essential part of agricultural history. From them a clear picture of the husbandry of the time is obtained and it is quite evident that farmers were becoming very concerned about grass. The meadows of Leicestershire, Northamptonshire, Devon and Somerset brought forth ecstatic praise and it is significant that by A.D. 1600 graziers were obviously men of substance, and wealthy classes of butchers and tanners were arising. The records of the period abound in such cases as the Earl of Derby, whose household in 1590 consumed 56 oxen and 535 sheep, while that of Sir William Fairfax in Yorkshire consumed 49 oxen and 150 sheep, and the household of the Bishop of Aberdeen consumed 48 oxen, 160 sheep, and 17 pigs. Fresh meat in winter was for the wealthy only, for the problem of feeding cattle and sheep on a large scale during the winter months still remained to be solved; the poor, when they had meat in winter, had to make do with salted. England lagged behind the times on this problem, for the value of turnips for cattle during the winter months was already appreciated in the Low Countries.

Wheat as an economic crop offers many attractions to farmers with suitable land and many of the enclosed pastures which had carried cattle and sheep for many years and had as a result increased appreciably in fertility were ploughed, and good yields were obtained which were markedly better than the medieval yield from the open fields, which was recorded as being a meagre 10 bushels per acre. A statute of 1597 had given official recognition to the fact that worn-out arable land regained its fertility when it was laid down to pasture and devoted to grazing stock for a number of years.

We do not know exactly when grass and clover became regarded as a crop and part of a recognised rotation. Richard Weston, a refugee from the Civil War, brought back from Holland a bag of red clover seed when he returned to England. The Spaniards had initiated the Dutch into the growing of red clover (*Trifolium pratense*) a century before and it was usually sown as a pure crop in the arable rotation. In 1653, Andrew Tarranton wrote *The Great Improvement of Lands by Clover* and, following much of the advice of Weston and Blyth, gave practical demonstrations of its value for stock feed, either when grazed or made into hay. He also managed to convey something of the fertility-restoring powers of clover and the immense increase in the stock-carrying capacity of clover pastures compared with ordinary grass. He instanced the need for careful control of the grazing to avoid the distressing trouble of "bloat" or "hoven" in which affected animals became "blown up" due to an accumulation of gas in the stomach resulting from failure of the mechanism which normally enables relief to be secured by belching. The trouble usually occurs when animals are suddenly introduced to young rich herbage and unfortunately it may prove fatal within an hour or so. (It is interesting to record that some three hundred years later we have not yet found a wholly reliable remedy.) Finally, he encouraged other farmers to visit him and see his ideas put into practice, and to-day we are broadly speaking still following the technique which he practised.

Progress was slow and more than a hundred years elapsed before the first stages in ley farming were generally adopted. The Society for the Encouragement of the Arts, Manufactures and Commerce did much to encourage land improvement and indeed in 1763 imported the seed of cocksfoot (*Dactylis glomerata*) from Virginia and also offered awards for the best herbage seed crops grown in this country. Benjamin Stillingfleet, in his *Calendar of Flora* 1762, invented English (as opposed to Latin) names for such species as had not already acquired them. Unfortunately, he included sweet vernal (*Anthoxanthum odoratum*) and other useless grasses amongst those recommended as valuable for agricultural purposes. This error was still unnoted 150 years later when excellent samples of this weed were offered for sale as a useful "bottom grass" by the agricultural merchants of the day.

The saving of good seed each year has been stressed by agricultural writers from earliest times. In the eighteenth century Coke of Norfolk and the Duke of Bedford employed children to go into the fields and hedgerows and collect the seed heads of different grasses when they were ripe, in order to have available a store of seed for sowing the following year.

During the latter half of the eighteenth century, agricultural progress was rapid. Tillage methods underwent revolutionary changes, substantial sums of money were invested in farm implements and machinery, in drainage and buildings, and every effort was made to improve both crops and livestock. Agricultural Societies were established all over the country and many of these are still in existence.

After the Napoleonic wars agriculture went into decline. The Board of Agriculture was dissolved in 1822.

When the virgin and fertile lands of the New World came into full production, causing a fall in world grain prices, the British farmer had to face a very real challenge. United Kingdom agriculture turned to dairy farming and animal husbandry generally. A good deal of land was allowed to revert to grass, buildings were not maintained, drainage was neglected, and sheep and cattle as alternative sources of income took the place of corn. By 1874, a vast acreage of arable land had been sown down to grass, no less than 1,688,487 acres between 1877 and 1884. Agriculturists were greatly concerned with the sowing down of land to permanent pasture and so we have J. Caird in his *English Agriculture* (1850) and M. H. Sutton (*Laying Down Land to Permanent Pasture*, 1861), J. Howard (*Laying Down Land to Grass*, 1880), C. de L. Faunce-De Laune (*On Laying Land to Permanent Grass*, 1882) and William Carruthers (*On Laying Land to Permanent Grass*, 1883) all in the Journal of the Royal Agricultural Society, devoting much attention to the problem but indicating at the same time that the tide would turn, that permanent grassland would again be ploughed for cropping and that the crops would be the better if good grassland had been established. The whole matter was summarised very effectively in Robert H. Elliott's book *The Clifton Park System of Farming* (1898).

In 1889 the Board of Agriculture was re-established, and in 1896, the classical experiments at Cockle Park, Northumberland, were initiated to demonstrate the value of basic slag as a source of phosphoric acid for the grass sward. Basic slag, superphosphate, and combinations of lime, slag, potash and nitrate of soda were under trial, the merit of the fertiliser being assessed by the liveweight increase of sheep which grazed the plots, or by the weight of hay. The outstanding treatment was an application of 10 cwt. per acre of basic slag as a first dressing, followed by 5 cwt. per acre every third year afterwards and this treatment was adopted by large numbers of farmers throughout the country. The effect of the slag was to so encourage the growth of wild white clover that the stock-carrying capacity of the grassland was increased threefold. Even to-day, it is quite common to find farmers using slag in these amounts.

By now attention was being given to the value of native strains of grasses in addition to wild white clover, and work at the North of Scotland College of Agriculture, and by Professor A. N. McAlpine at Glasgow, had indicated something of the potential of grass output when the right types of grasses were linked to wise fertilising. In 1919, Lord Milford, by a generous gift to the University College of Wales at Aberystwyth, brought into being the Welsh Plant Breeding Station which, under its director Professor R. G. Stapledon, was to make a far-reaching contribution to the realm of grassland husbandry in the production of leafy, indigenous strains of the principal grasses. Their names to-day carry the prefix "S" and are known throughout the world.

Other land-marks in the history of grassland in this country are the establishment of Jealott's Hill Research Station in Berkshire by Imperial Chemical Industries in 1936, the formation of the British Grassland Society in 1945, and the opening of the Grassland Research Institute at Hurley in Berkshire in 1949, the first station to be devoted solely to fundamental research problems in the sphere of grassland husbandry.

Spectacular progress has been made in British agriculture during the past quarter-century. It has become much more productive, has reached a high level of technical efficiency and is probably the most highly mechanised in the world. The acute dangers of two world wars and their aftermath have indicated the vital national need to reduce the dependence of a very large industrial population upon imported food supplies.

The need for maximum self-sufficiency in terms of home-grown feeding-stuffs has placed greater and greater emphasis on the production of more and better grass and upon its more efficient utilisation by grazing and conservation. A greater cattle population has thus been maintained at a higher level of output of both milk and beef, and there has been a marked revival in the sheep industry.

CHAPTER 3

THE GRASS PLANT AND ITS VALUE TO MAN

In this chapter I shall begin with a brief description of the various parts of a grass plant, emphasising the features that are of importance to agriculture. A fuller and more detailed account may be found in Dr. Hubbard's excellent Penguin volume *Grasses* (1954).

To the non-botanist all grasses look very much like one another at first sight. On closer inspection, however, differences in habit and form of growth and particularly of inflorescence are very apparent. There are grasses which are Lilliputian in size, contrasting violently with the largest members of the family, the bamboos, bearing great masses of blooms on spikes or panicles a foot or more long. Grasses, too, display an immense capacity for adapting themselves to their environment, some making their home in water or along the banks of streams and rivers, while others survive the scorching heat of the desert and or the intense cold of the polar regions. Some grasses are annual and complete their life cycle in one year, such as the very common annual meadow grass (*Poa annua*). Others like the soft brome grass (*Bromus mollis*) are biennial, the seed germinating in late summer or autumn and the plant flowering and seeding the following year. Finally, there are vast numbers of perennials, like perennial ryegrass (*Lolium perenne*) and couch grass (*Agropyron repens*), which are potentially immortal, producing new shoots or new lengths of rhizomes for ever if conditions allow. A bamboo may survive for thirty or forty years or even longer. Unlike the annuals and biennials, which bear flower-heads on all or most of the shoots, in the perennials the flowering shoots are accompanied by vegetative shoots, the number of which depends upon the duration of the grass.

These vegetative and flowering shoots are not different in origin. Both shoots start off as a vegetative structure—a very short-jointed stem bearing two ranks of leaves, one leaf at each of its closely-spaced joints or nodes and arranged alternately along the stem, which is

15

constantly producing new leaves at its tip; thus there is a continuous sequence of growth. As each leaf reaches full size the older ones die away, to be replaced by fresh leaves. Meanwhile the stem remains extremely short, but branching often takes place. Buds in the axils of the leaves grow out to form a new short-stemmed leafy shoot, and these in turn produce further shoots in the axils of their leaves, so that a dense tuft is quickly built up. This process of increase in the number of shoots, without any marked lengthening of the stem, is particularly noticeable in young cereal plants during the first few months of growth, and has been given the special name of "tillering," each shoot being referred to as a "tiller." Obviously tillering capacity in the cereals means that less seed per acre needs to be sown than would be the case were only a single shoot formed from each seed. If each tiller produced an ear to be harvested flowering would be spread over a long period, hence ripening would be very uneven and farming operations complicated; but the normal wheat-field is sown thickly so that only one or two of the earliest-formed tillers on each plant are able to flower, which ensures that all the ears of grain are ready for cutting at the same time. Pastures, on the other hand, produce more stock food since the grasses cover the ground more rapidly to form a sward or turf, and recover from mechanical damage comparatively quickly because of this characteristic.

A turf of vegetative shoots may be a foot or more in height, but it consists almost entirely of leaf. The stems are still extremely short and completely hidden, so that in a typically tufted grass at this stage of growth all the stems and buds are within about half an inch of the ground. It is only in exceptionally tall-growing grasses, such as the bamboos, that long, upright vegetative stems are produced at an early stage. In the case of creeping grasses there may be some elongated stems but these are horizontally directed and spread along or through the ground as stolons or rhizomes. By way of contrast, the lower internodes of some grasses may become swollen with plant food, and these grasses are known as "bulbous."

This characteristic of the grasses—the growth-buds remaining close to the ground—determines their value as food for grazing animals. If an upright-growing plant, like kale or a young tree seedling, is grazed off to within an inch or two of the ground it will have lost the greater part of its stem, together with its apical bud and most of its axillary buds. It may recover by the development of new shoots from the base of the stem, but it is unlikely to survive many such grazings. In marked contrast to this a vegetative grass plant grazed

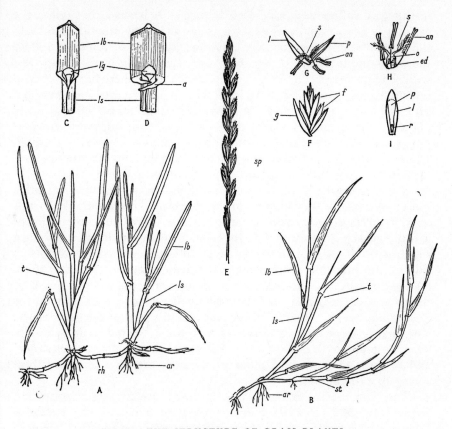

FIG I. THE STRUCTURE OF GRASS PLANTS

A grass plant with rhizomes (*Poa pratensis*)
B grass plant with stolons (*Agrostis stolonifera*)
C leaf without auricles (*Poa pratensis*)
D leaf with auricles (*Lolium multiflorum*)
E inflorescence (spike of *Lolium perenne*)
F spikelet (*Lolium perenne*)
G floret
H flower
I "seed"

a	auricle	*l*	lemma	*r*	rachilla
an	anther	*lb*	leaf blade	*rh*	rhizome
ar	adventitious roots	*ed*	lodicule	*s*	style
f	floret	*lg*	ligule	*sp*	spikelet
g	glume (concealing	*ls*	leaf sheath	*st*	stolon
	lemma of adjacent	*o*	ovary	*t*	tiller
	floret)	*p*	palea		

in this way suffers very much less damage. It is clear that unless the grazing is exceptionally close as a result of many animal mouths to the acre or continuous stocking, only the leaves will be removed and all the stems and buds will be left intact and able to continue their growth with comparatively little check. Grasses can therefore withstand repeated grazing and treading by stock. In the face of such grazing, grasses obviously have a great advantage over other taller-growing plants; indeed, except where drought or extreme exposure prevents the growth of taller plants, grassland exists mainly because of grazing. If there were no grazing animals there would be, in a climate like that of Britain, very little grassland, only scrub and forest.

Grass shoots do not, however, remain indefinitely in this vegetative stage; eventually they change to the flowering condition. When this occurs the stem apex ceases to produce new leaves and instead forms a rudimentary inflorescence. Once this change has taken place in a shoot, it produces no more new leaves and no more axillary shoots or tillers; the inflorescence develops, the stem elongates to bring it up above the level of the leaves, the flowers are pollinated, the fruit ripens and is shed, and the whole shoot dies. Growth of the plant is then continued by other tillers which are still in the vegetative state. The change from the vegetative stage to the flowering stage is usually a response to length of day; most British grasses are "long day plants" and so these changes take place in them as the days lengthen from spring to early summer.

The tiller must, however, have reached a certain size before it can respond to the increasing hours of daylight and this size varies in different grasses. If a small tiller can respond, then all the tillers will reach the necessary size during the year, before the days become too short again. In this case therefore all tillers will flower and die. Thus there will be no vegetative tillers left to continue growth and the plant behaves as an annual. If, however, the tiller cannot respond until it has reached a larger size, it will not flower until the late summer (aftermath flowering) or it may not flower that year. If, as is true of some grasses, a period of low temperature is necessary before response can take place, flowering will be delayed until the following spring. Meantime, the tiller, while still in the vegetative condition, will have produced further tillers so that the plant behaves as a long-lived perennial. Such plants produce some flowering shoots each year but always remain sufficiently vegetative to ensure continued growth.

With few exceptions grasses have fibrous roots—in some species they are tough and cord-like—which arise adventitiously from the

PLATE 1. Grassland country. The view from Long Mynd in Shropshire — a typical hedge-patterned English landscape with a wealth of trees indicating an adequate rainfall

PLATE 2. Cornfields near Thornbill in Shropshire, with oats in the stook

lowermost node or nodes of the stem. This capacity of grasses to produce numerous fibrous roots is of prime importance for it means that grasses, unlike plants with a main tap root, have great powers of recovery after injury. When the main tap root of such a plant is injured the plant probably dies; root injuries to grasses on the other hand may even stimulate new growth. Thus severe harrowing of an old pasture with heavy spiked harrows, which cut into the turf, tears out much of the matted growth, increases aeration, and brings about rejuvenation, with the result that the pasture "freshens up" with new growth. Similarly the groundsman, using "pruning" machines on the sports turf or lawn, encourages new, strong root and leaf development.

The roots of different species vary in length and are equipped with a very great number of root hairs. In some cases, like couch grass, underground, scaly, whitish or brownish creeping stems or rhizomes are formed and both roots and scale leaves are produced from the nodes of these rhizomes. In other cases, like creeping bent (*Agrostis stolonifera*) and rough-stalked meadow-grass (*Poa trivialis*), thin, greenish or purplish, surface-creeping stems or stolons, like strawberry runners, are formed from the nodes, from which fibrous roots and green leaves are produced. Thus rhizomes and stolons are really modified stems, and grasses with such rooting, mat-forming systems cover the ground very rapidly in consequence. Such a characteristic is not always desirable and in some cases it presents serious problems. Any bud-bearing portion of a rhizome which is broken off from the root system can start a new and independent plant. Thus couch grass which can be a very serious weed on some types of arable land, becomes a menace by the very speed with which it reproduces itself. The small pieces of rhizome broken and dispersed in the course of cultivation give rise to new colonies of plants and it is not unknown for the growth of couch to be so great that the intended crop is smothered. Moreover, the diversion of food materials to the formation of such non-photosynthetic and inedible structures as stolons and rhizomes has the effect of reducing the maximum yield, and such grasses as bent and couch are, therefore, most unproductive. The highest yielding agricultural grasses, such as the ryegrasses, cocksfoot and timothy, are tufted, non-creeping species.

The flowering stems ("culms") of the grasses are usually cylindrical and hollow except at the nodes or joints, where the stem is firm and solid and from where the leaves emanate. Culms vary not only in size, rigidity and number of nodes but may grow erect, prostrate or arise from a curved or prostrate base. The stems are usually smooth and highly polished. The leaves are parallel-veined and arranged in two rows alternating one with another on the stem. Each leaf is composed of a lower portion known as the "sheath" which may form a cylindrical tube enclosing the stem, or may be split, with the margins overlapping one another. Near the ground, the sheath may be coloured red, purple or brown which is constant for each species and constitutes an aid to identification. In some species, only the veins are coloured. The upper portion of each leaf is called the "blade"; this may be flat, rolled up and bristle-like, or folded about the mid-rib with the upper surface inwards, while the blades may be erect, drooping, or at right angles to the sheath. The blade, usually long and narrow with parallel sides or tapering to a pointed or blunt tip, often widens out at its base to form either a ledge or ear-like projections or teeth called "auricles," which clasp the stem. Where the blade joins the sheath there is usually a membranous outgrowth, called the "ligule," which may be pointed, blunt or ragged, long or short, or may be represented by a line of hairs. These characteristics afford still further means of identification. The leaves of some grasses are hairy, others free from hairs (glabrous); if present, the hairs may be most abundant on the sheath, on the upper or lower surfaces of the leaf blade or, in some instances, confined to the ribs or margins.

This key to the identification of the commoner pasture grasses by means of their vegetative characters has been compiled to enable the enthusiast when walking over a farm to distinguish the chief species making up the swards. It has been made as simple as possible and deals with only a few of the better known grasses. Readers who wish to identify a much wider range of species should consult Hubbard's *Grasses* (1954).

KEY FOR IDENTIFICATION OF COMMON GRASSES WHEN NOT IN FLOWER

1 Leaf-blades more or less flat, breadth greater than
   thickness.   2
   Leaf-blades bristle-like.   17
2 Shoot flat or oval, young leaves folded.   3
   Shoot round, young leaves rolled.   7
3 Base of leaf-sheath coloured, blades ribbed on
   upper surface.   4
   Base of leaf-sheath white, blades not ribbed.   5
4 Leaf-sheath red.   *Lolium perenne*
   Leaf-sheath yellow.   *Cynosurus cristatus*
5 Leaf-sheath thick, fleshy, blades broad, tapering.   *Dactylis glomerata*
   Leaf-sheath thin. leaf-blades narrower.   6

6 Leaves tapering, pale-green, soft; plant perennial with short creeping stems on surface.	*Poa trivialis*
Leaves parallel-sided, dark-green, stiff; plant perennial with underground creeping stems.	*Poa pratensis*
Leaves short; plant annual, tufted.	*Poa annua*
7 Hooks (auricles) present at junction of leaf-blade and sheath.	8
Auricles absent.	11
8 Base of leaf-sheath red; blades ribbed on upper surface, shiny under surface.	9
Base of leaf-sheath white; blades dull, somewhat hairy. White creeping stems below ground.	*Agropyron repens*
9 Plant short-lived, old leaf-sheaths not persisting.	*Lolium multiflorum*
Plant perennial, old dead leaf-sheaths present at base.	10
10 Plant small, smooth, auricles not fringed.	*Festuca pratensis*
Plant large, harsh, auricles fringed.	*Festuca arundinacea*
11 Plant tufted or only slightly spreading.	12
Plant strongly creeping.	*Agrostis* sp.
12 Leaves without hairs.	13
Leaves hairy.	14
13 Shoot base bulbous, pale, ligule short, pointed.	*Phleum pratense*
Shoot base not swollen, old sheaths dark brown, ligule blunt.	*Alopecurus pratensis*
14 Sheath not split.	*Bromus mollis*
Sheath split.	15
15 Veins of sheath red.	*Holcus lanatus*
Veins of sheath not red.	16
16 Hairs scattered, blade very long, roots yellow.	*Arrhenatherum elatius*
Hairs on sheath pointing down.	*Trisetum flavescens*
Conspicuous tuft of hairs at top of sheath.	*Anthoxanthum odoratum*
17 Sheath split; plant tufted.	*Festuca ovina*
Sheath not split; plant usually creeping.	*Festuca rubra* spp. *rubra*

The inflorescence varies widely in the different genera and, if present, is the easiest means of identification. It is made up of a varying number of "partial" inflorescences called spikelets, each of which is composed of one or more flowers, each with two enveloping protective structures, the lemma and the palea. In most cases the grass flowers bear both stamens and pistil but in maize (*Zea mays*), for instance, the male flower is produced in the "tassel" and the female on the "cob" with its greatly thickened axis. Very rarely male and female flowers may be borne on different plants, as in buffalo grass (*Buchloe dactyloides*).

The form of inflorescence is determined according to the way spikelets are arranged on the stem. The spikelets may be borne directly on the main axis to form a spike as in the ryegrass or couch grass; they may be borne on simple branches to give a raceme, as in false brome (*Brachypodium* spp.), or, as in the majority of grasses, borne on secondary, tertiary or even more sub-divided branches to give a panicle. The length and stoutness of the branches provide a wide variety of panicles between the extremes of an erect, close inflorescence, superficially resembling a spike, as in foxtail (*Alopecurus* spp.) or timothy, and one which is long and drooping, loose and spreading, like the bromes.

Flowering usually takes place from May to July, although in mild winters a number of species develop flower-heads in December or even January. Annual meadow grass, on the other hand, can generally be seen in bloom throughout the year. The first grass to flower in the spring is holy grass (*Hierochloë odorata*), which is in bloom about the end of March, but this species is very rare in the British Isles, and is confined to three Scottish counties and one Irish. Meadow foxtail (*Alopecurus pratensis*) and sweet vernal grass may flower in April, the ryegrasses in May, cocksfoot and the fescues in June, and timothy in July. Woodland and mountain species are somewhat later in flowering than species of the same genera growing in more open habitats or at lower altitudes. The early-flowering grasses are usually those in which only a comparatively short day is required for flower initiation; the later are those needing a longer day.

Since the actual flowers of grasses are very simple and show comparatively little variation, classification and identification have to depend largely on the structure and arrangement of the spikelets. Each true flower consists only of a single pistil with (usually) two styles, and (usually) three stamens, plus, in most grasses, a pair of minute scales which are known as "lodicules" and which have been regarded as representing very reduced sepals. Each flower is protected by two much larger structures, the inner, usually two-keeled, palea and the round, single-keeled, lemma. The lemma and palea fit closely together over the flower and are only separated for a short time when the lodicules swell up temporarily, pressing them apart, and allowing the styles and stamens to protrude and wind-pollination to take place.

Each true flower plus its lemma and palea is known as a "floret" and the spikelet consists of from one to about twenty florets. At its base there are two (occasionally one or none) protective structures, the glumes. Both the lemmas and the glumes may be furnished with bristles (awns), which are useful features for identification.

The following key will enable the more important species to be identified in the flowering stage.

KEY FOR IDENTIFICATION OF COMMON GRASSES WHEN IN FLOWER

1 Inflorescence a spike; spikelets not stalked.   2
   Inflorescence a raceme. One very shortly-stalked, many-flowered spikelet at each node.   *Brachypodium* spp.
   Inflorescence a panicle (spikelets on long or short branched stalks).   7

2 Spike branched.   *Spartina* spp.
   Spike not branched.   3

3 One spikelet at each node.   4
   Two spikelets at each node. Spike large, spikelets several-flowered.   *Elymus arenarius*
   Three spikelets at each node. Spikelets one-flowered, central one only fertile.   *Hordeum* spp.

4 Spike one-sided; spikelets one-flowered.   *Nardus stricta*
   Spike not one-sided; spikelets several-flowered.   5

5 Spikelet placed edgewise; 1 glume only.   6
   Spikelet placed sideways on; 2 glumes.   *Agropyron repens*
       (Wheat 3 or more large florets and broad glumes, lemmas usually awnless, and Rye with two large florets and narrow glumes, lemmas always awned, come here)

6 Lemmas awnless.   *Lolium perenne*
   Lemmas awned.   *Lolium multiflorum*

7 Spikelets usually many-flowered (4 or more); glumes short, not hiding florets.   8
   Spikelets few-flowered (2-5 usually); glumes long, concealing at least the lower florets.   19
   Spikelets one-flowered; glumes long, concealing floret.   23

8 Panicle branches mainly spreading.   9
   Panicle branches very short, not spreading, so that inflorescence looks more like spike. Sterile skeleton spikelets present as well as fertile.   *Cynosurus cristatus*

9 Lemmas with awn on back.   10
   Lemmas awnless or with awn on tip.   11

10 Lemmas rounded, spikelet oval.   *Bromus mollis* & related species
   Lemmas keeled, spikelet triangular.   *Bromus sterilis* & related species

11 Lemmas with rounded back.   12
   Lemmas keeled on back.   16

12 Lemmas very blunt.   13
   Lemmas bluntly or sharply pointed or shortly awned.   14

13 Spikelets long, cylindrical.   *Glyceria fluitans*
   Spikelets short, rounded-triangular.   *Briza media*

14 Panicle purple, usually long and slender, stigma
and anthers dark purple. *Molinia caerulea*

Panicle green, becoming brown or yellowish.
Stigma and anthers pale. 15

15 Panicle and florets small. *Festuca ovina* & *F. rubra*

Panicle and florets larger, two branches at most
nodes, with 1 or 2 spikelets on smaller branch,
lemmas bluntly pointed. *Festuca pratensis*

Panicle very large, 3 or more spikelets on smaller
branch, lemmas with awn-point. *Festuca arundinacea*

16 Lemmas straight, bluntly pointed. 17

Lemmas curved, with awn point, panicle large
with dense clumps of spikelets. *Dactylis glomerata*

17 Panicle small, no "web." *Poa annua*

Panicle larger, "web" of cottony hairs at base of
lemma. 18

18 Spikelets rather small, panicle open, light and
feathery in appearance. *Poa trivialis*

Spikelets slightly larger, panicle closer, denser and
heavier in appearance. *Poa pratensis*

19 Panicle branches mainly spreading. Spikelet erect. 20

Panicle branches short, not spreading. Spikelet of
one shiny fertile floret and two sterile brown
hairy awned lemmas. *Anthoxanthum odoratum*

20 Spikelets two-flowered, one fertile, one male only. 21

Spikelets with two or more fertile florets. 22

21 Spikelets fairly large, lower floret male with
prominent bent awn, upper floret fertile. *Arrhenatherum elatius*

Spikelets small, lower floret fertile, upper floret
male with small fish-hook awn. *Holcus lanatus*

(*Holcus mollis* similar but with more prominent
bent awn)

22 Panicle rather small, closing in fruit, yellow,
spikelets 2-5 flowered. *Trisetum flavescens*

(*Helictotrichon* spp. with larger spikelets would
also come here)

Panicle spreading, purplish-brown, branches wavy,
spikelets small, two-flowered. *Deschampsia flexuosa*

Panicle spreading, very large, often silvery, spikelets smaller, two-flowered. *Deschampsia caespitosa*

23 Panicle somewhat spreading, spikelets very small. 24

Panicle always closed, densely cylindrical, spike-
like. 25

Panicle large, cylindrical, tapering, spikelets very
large, (on sand dunes). *Ammophila arenaria*

24 Panicle open in flower, closing in fruit.	*Agrostis stolonifera*
Panicle open throughout.	*Agrostis tenuis*
(*Agrostis canina* and *A. gigantea* would also come here)	
25 Glumes stiffly-pointed, floret short, unawned, threshing out when ripe.	*Phleum pratense*
Glumes blunt, joined at base, floret awned and enclosed by glumes.	25
26 Panicle stout, spikelet oval, hairy.	*Alopecurus pratensis*
Panicle slender, spikelet oblong, not hairy.	*Alopecurus myosuroides*

Grasses show an amazing tolerance to external conditions. For instance sheep's fescue, which grows down to sea level in this country, has also been recorded on the highest mountains in Britain and at nearly 18,000 ft. in the Himalayas. Then again, many grasses from low-lying habitats in temperate regions adapt themselves to high altitudes in tropical countries. Others survive wide differences of climate, the classic example of adaptability being perhaps sweet vernal grass, which flourishes from sea level to above the snow line, is equally at home on sand, loam or clay, and is found in many countries of the world with vastly different climates, ranging from North Africa to Siberia.

A number of other grasses are on the other hand very specialised in their habitats. Moor mat grass is usually associated with the margins of peat moors, not because it will not grow elsewhere, but because it grows better under such conditions than any other. A number of grasses can endure strong salt water, such as marram grass (*Ammophila arenaria*), the salt marsh grasses (*Puccinellia* spp.), and sea lyme grass (*Elymus arenarius*), and these are confined to our coasts. Marram and sea lyme are used for stabilising wind-blown sand, while the salt marsh grasses and rice grass (*Spartina townsendii*) are mudbinding plants of salt marshes.

Other grasses adapt themselves well to a high water content in the soil, and "water meadows," where periodic and controlled flooding was carried out, were in use until quite recent times. To a limited extent this is still practised in Wiltshire and Dorset. The operative phrase is "controlled flooding" for good drainage of the soil is imperative for the growth of the best types of grasses useful to the farmer. Under waterlogged conditions the deficiency of an adequate air supply to the plant roots spells failure for the ryegrasses, cocksfoot, timothy, rough stalked meadow grass, and similar productive species.

Under such conditions tussock grass (*Deschampsia caespitosa*), rushes (*Juncus* spp.) and sedges (*Carex* spp.), which are inedible for livestock, become dominant.

The true seed of grasses is not normally seen, since the fruit-coat is very thin and firmly attached to the single seed. This type of fruit is known as a caryopsis: a wheat grain is a good example. Most grass "seeds" consist of a single grain tightly enclosed within the lemma and palea; attached to the base is generally a small portion of the axis of the spikelet. In the case of Yorkshire fog, meadow foxtail, and a number of other grasses the "seed" is, however, an entire spikelet and consists of the two glumes, and the lemma, palea and grain of one or more flowers, while in the case of the brown "seed" of timothy and most wheats the grain is shed free from its lemma and palea. The bulk of timothy seed, however, is the silver grey "seed" composed of the caryopsis complete with lemma and palea. These examples illustrate how the grass "seed"—that part of the plant which is actually sown either naturally or in agricultural practice—differs from the true seed.

Grasses are distributed in the main by the wind, for the caryopses with their enclosing glumes are light and capable of being carried long distances. Some seeds are plumed, others possess tufts of hairs which doubtless increase their buoyancy. Gales and whirlwinds are likely to exert a great influence in conveying seeds from one place to another. In Lincolnshire, for instance, a whirlwind has been known to tear up a tuft of couch grass by the roots and carry it for over twenty miles, and it has been suggested that since gale force winds are common during the period July to September, when many grasses are seeding, they must be a very important means of dispersal and probably of greater influence than normal wind-drift.

One must not overlook the influence of water in carrying grass seeds long distances. Their buoyancy in the air is equalled in many cases by their facility in floating on water, while the upper peduncles act as sails to assist them in their passage across estuaries and round coasts. In addition too, it is not unknown for whole plants to be transported by the sea and it is recorded that the sugar cane on Cocos Keeling Island was derived from a clump from Java, seven hundred miles away. Bamboos have also been known to be moved from place to place. Drifting rhizomes in rivers and in the sea also bring about dispersal and in Europe, *Puccinellia maritima*, *Elymus arenarius* and *Ammophila arenaria* are known to be dispersed by these means. Tufts of annual meadow grass are often carried long distances by rivers and indeed, of all grasses this is perhaps the most determined to establish itself by some means or another. At Seale Hayne it is regularly removed from the roof gutters and spoutings thirty feet above ground level. It springs up between cobblestones and flags in the heart of our largest industrial cities and I have found it growing in birds' nests in late autumn after the nests have been abandoned and are well soaked with rain. This is particularly the case in thrushes' nests which are mud-lined. It has also been found 12,000 feet up in the Himalayas where it was concluded that man or his yak must have been the means of conveyance. The glumes of some grasses bear stiff reflexed spines which help the seeds to cling to clothing, to the wool or fur of animals, or to the feathers of birds. In the Belgian Congo termites store large quantities of a species of *Cynodon* in their nests and when these are abandoned the grass is established. I heard of a most interesting case when in New Zealand, where man quite unwittingly was the means of introducing red-top. Emigrants before leaving Nova Scotia filled their mattresses with hay which included red-top. They travelled to the Cape of Good Hope, thence to Australia, and finally settled in New Zealand where the mattresses were abandoned; the grass seeds germinated and thus an American grass became established in a strange country!

The farmer classifies a grass as useful or useless according to its particular value to him. There are over a hundred and fifty different species of British grasses but of these no more than twenty are of real agricultural value and indeed, on the majority of farms, considerably fewer are regarded as of consequence.

The value of grass to the farmer depends upon (a) productivity, or yield, (b) feeding value or chemical composition, (c) palatability, (d) persistency, (e) winter greenness and (f) earliness. To the groundsman, however, it is obvious that such factors as (a) slowness of growth, and (b) wearing capacity and ability to recover from harsh treatment, are of much more importance, while the landscape gardener must also look for very different qualities in grasses to form ornamental lawns or for foliage work in border and greenhouse. Quite naturally, in the case of both groundsman and gardener, the species used are often different from those used in agriculture, and in these pages I have concentrated on the latter.

The yield of herbage produced by any grass, which is the farmer's first consideration in making a selection, depends upon its tillering capacity, the facility with which it recovers from cutting or grazing, and the duration of growth each season. An excellent illustration is obtained by comparing perennial ryegrass and bent grass. The former tillers freely and grows steadily from early spring until late in the autumn and indeed, in the mild wet south-west of England it grows all the year round. In contrast to this, bent grass grows for a short period only and yields comparatively little bulk, and in consequence is discarded by the farmer as being of no value. To him it is in fact a weed.

Then the ability of a grass to recover from cutting or grazing is also of great importance, defoliation being more favourable to the development of young tillers in some species than in others. Recent work has tended to stress the importance of the influence of intensity of defoliation on the yielding capacity of grasses. It appears that by leaving some growth—say one to two inches—when cutting or grazing a sward, more rapid recovery of growth follows, and hence more bulk or weight of grass over the whole season is obtained, than when animals are allowed to graze tightly to the ground or the mowing machine blades are set as closely as possible to the bare earth. The full answer is not yet known, for species vary in this respect and are also subject to seasonal variations.

While most grasses are palatable if eaten in the early stages of growth, quite a number develop harsh or hairy leaves, or even spines on the leaf margins, as they grow older, and hence are rejected by stock. A grass which may be highly valuable in all other respects can be rendered useless by this factor; Yorkshire fog and the coarser forms of tall fescue are typical examples. In practice it is not always possible to utilise a field at the ideal stage of growth, when the grass is most palatable to stock, and thus grasses which retain their palatability over a long period are particularly valuable. Yield and feeding value are complementary factors, the one without the other being useless to the farmer. In this connection the structure of the grass is important, for species with a high proportion of leaf to stem are much more valuable than stemmy ones, since the leaves are more palatable and contain more protein than the stalks. Grasses become coarse and stemmy with a corresponding reduction in feeding value as they reach the seeding stage. Plant breeders of recent years have endeavoured, therefore, to produce strains of grasses with a high proportion of leaf to stem and with a natural reluctance to produce flowering heads.

From the farming angle as well as the ornamental, a capacity to remain green during the winter months is important. This extends the grazing season and reduces the need for expensive artificial feeding of livestock. Certain varieties of meadow foxtail and red fescue, for instance, have been bred to produce leafage during February and March.

In the last thirty years a great deal of attention has been paid to variations of type within each grass species. Perennial ryegrass, for example, may be tufted, stemmy and short-lived or it may be leafy and persistent. Some types are very prostrate in growth whilst others are erect. Some are very palatable, others less so. The same comments are applicable to all the important species of commercial value such as cocksfoot, timothy, and meadow fescue, and these are classified into what are technically known as "cultivars" (but more familiarly as varieties or strains), and multiplication by division and seed of these strains is carried out on a large scale.

It is very evident there can be no simple answer to the question, "Which is the best grass?" Quite apart from the great variations which we have seen exist within the grasses themselves, the complexity of the problem is magnified by varying systems of management whether for grazing or conservation, by the use of different seeds mixtures, by fertiliser and herbicidal treatment, by disease and insect pest, and by the varying requirements of sheep and cattle. The whole fascinating study is unfolded in the following chapters.

CHAPTER 4

TYPES OF BRITISH GRASSLAND

Centuries of biotic influence have brought about the formation of our so-called natural types of grassland, for even the wild stretches of hill and moorland, which to most people epitomise natural grassland, owe their existence to the influence of countless generations of grazing animals, particularly sheep. Without man's influence heather, bracken, and scrubby growth soon colonise the land to act as the forerunners of bush, pine and rowan until a dense forest growth occupies the countryside. Let us, therefore, be precise and speak of uncultivated and cultivated grassland. The former group includes moors, downs, wolds, heaths and fens, broadly termed rough grazings, while the latter includes the rich permanent pastures and meadows which are "cultivated" by regular mechanical treatment with harrows and rollers and receive periodic applications of the essential plant nutrients though the turf is left undisturbed. Included in this group is the ley or short duration grassland which is ploughed periodically. The subdivisions are clearly seen in table 4:

TABLE 4. SUBDIVISIONS OF GRASSLAND

Uncultivated grassland		Cultivated grassland	
moors:	(north and west of Britain)	permanent	temporary
downs:	(south and east)	pastures	leys
heaths:	(south and east)	and	of
fens:	(mainly in the east)	meadows	varying
			duration

The transition from ley to permanent pasture or meadows, thence to rough grazing and scrub, and finally to forest, is an orderly, gradual process, the different phases being clearly recognisable yet merging one with another. The great areas of rough grazings are known to all countrymen and townsmen alike and a brief outline of the different types of grassland in this group will give added interest to the countryside.

The soil of our moorland areas, including those of Scotland and the Lake District, the Pennines, the Yorkshire moors of the north-east, the Welsh mountains, and the moors of Cornwall, Devon and Somerset, is acid or "sour" and a marked lime shortage is invariably associated with a deficiency in phosphate and potash. Under such conditions our useful grasses and clovers cannot survive and the flora is very restricted and specialised, the degree of acidity, the rainfall and the drainage determining the specific type of herbage found in any particular stretch of moor. Free-draining land is often in close proximity to bog, but in the majority of cases the sterile condition of the soil has resulted in an accumulation of undecomposed vegetation, "mat," near the surface and the grassland is said to be "matted."

On the wetter soils the dominant species is often flying bent (*Molinia*), the long straws of which were once used by country people for making stiff carpet brushes. Should the peat be waterlogged then cotton grass, deer grass, heath or square-stemmed rush will be found in varying amounts. If the peat is well drained, as on hill sides and knolls, the soil still being very acid, then the dominant grass is mat-grass, so named because it grows in dense matted tufts, the hard bristle-like wiry leaves being much too tough for cattle or sheep to eat. Often associated with matgrass will be sheep's fescue, bilberry and heather. On really deep soil, which is fundamentally good land, bracken is frequently dominant, and when this land is cultivated it yields excellent crops of potatoes and oats. So runs the old adage, "Copper under Heather, Silver under Gorse, Gold under Bracken," which proved so true in the wartime ploughing-up campaign of 1939-45. Heather land yielded poor crops, even with generous fertiliser treatment, for the soil was too hungry and lacked body, whereas surprisingly good crops followed the ploughing in of bracken. Gorse land gave results somewhere between the heather and the bracken.

Heather moor is primarily sheep country and normally carries about one ewe to four or five acres. Hardy cattle, such as the Galloway, may sometimes be seen in association with sheep on the best moors. The periodic burning of the heather prevents the development of scrub and encourages new growth and, in late winter especially, young heather shoots are valuable in providing adequate sustenance for the sheep. When the burning is too slow, i.e. the fire does not sweep rapidly over the heather and the roots are damaged in consequence, bilberry frequently replaces the heather which represents the next phase in the succession.

The most valuable of the moorland or hill pastures contain sheep's fescue, red fescue and bent as the dominant species and although these grasses are at the bottom of the nutritional scale as we shall see, they have the advantage of demanding the minimum of attention from the farmer in order to keep a stable sward. Bracken is generally the most serious intruder but this can be kept in check with regular attention. On the moors of Cornwall and Devon rough uncultivated pastures contain *Agrostis setacea* as the dominant species. Very few clovers are ever seen in hill pastures.

Uncultivated downland pastures are unique for their extremely varied flora. While the chief grasses are sheep's fescue, erect brome and a number of oatgrasses (*Trisetum* and *Helictotrichon*), there is also a wide range of miscellaneous plants like yarrow and ribgrass, with the result that the herbage is very well liked by stock which thrive upon it. On the Cotswolds and other oolitic escarpments in many parts of the country, torgrass (*Brachypodium pinnatum*) is frequently dominant.

The heaths, the third type of uncultivated grassland, have a herbage which varies somewhat, depending upon their location. Sheep's fescue often dominates the sward with heather and sand sedge on the Brecklands of East Anglia and with Molinia, heather, bracken, and scrub on the Greensands and Eocene formations of the southern heaths. Heathland is hungry land and while it can yield good crops under good management they are costly to secure and the soil is expensive to maintain in a fertile condition, for the tendency to revert to scrub is always present. Fortunately, however, heath land is excellent for golf and race courses and other sporting activities.

As for fens, found chiefly in the east, these are peat soils which differ, however, from the peat of the moorland in having a high lime content. They are usually badly drained and because of the contours it is extremely difficult and costly to improve them. They cannot, therefore, be cultivated in a normal manner. They are usually colonised by Molinia, reed, sedges (*Cladium mariscus* and *Carex* spp.) with birch, alder, willow and other scrub where the neglect has been marked and the effect of the grazing animal sadly missed. As one might expect there is always a tendency to revert to swamp under such conditions.

Although of less value agriculturally one should perhaps mention at this point the seaside fescue pastures, estuarine salt-marshes and sand dunes. Marram grass is dominant on the dunes and frequently the only grass species present, while in salt marshes most people have admired the delightful sea lavenders which are often associated with the salt-marsh grass (*Puccinellia maritima*).

Although these moors, downs, heaths and fens are classified in the Agricultural Returns as rough grazings and may appear to the uninitiated in the nature of waste land, it must be remembered that some 16¾ million acres of land in the United Kingdom are covered by such herbage and form the rearing ground for much of our livestock. Sheep and cattle are annually sold at "fairs" and markets in large numbers to supply the needs of farmers owning good land, not only for breeding stock but for animals to finish for the butcher.

The area of rough grazing has remained more or less constant for the past twenty years or more and represents an immense potential reserve of productivity. It is true that the cultivation of these vast stretches of country, often of difficult contour, beset by problems of climate and soil fertility, would be expensive by comparison with lowland areas, and we have a big acreage of poor lowland grassland which must first be tackled; but should ever the need arise to bring our moorland areas into full productivity the task is by no means insuperable. To-day we have the technical knowledge and the equipment to bring about a startling transformation. Startling is not too strong a word, for in 1940 I was responsible for creating a green oasis of ryegrass and clover in the midst of a cotton grass moor. Milk cows grazed in fields which formerly had only had an occasional nibble from a hardy Scotch Blackface sheep!

As indicated in table 4 cultivated grassland may be subdivided into "permanent," and "temporary," which is usually termed ley. The permanent grassland may be subdivided into pastures, which in the main are devoted to the needs of the grazing animal, and meadows which are primarily used for raising hay. This line of demarcation is less clear-cut than it was thirty years ago when few farmers would have contemplated taking a crop of hay from a first-class pasture—although in the latter case, after a crop of hay had been taken in any particular year, the cattle and sheep were frequently allowed access to graze the "aftermath" or second growth of grass. This somewhat rigid adherence to grazing or mowing practice is to-day replaced by a much more flexible method of management which has been made possible by the increased knowledge available. With continued grazing, the finer pasture grasses, wild white clover, and miscellaneous herbs, are encouraged; whereas when a field is used exclusively year after year for hay, coarser, more bulky grasses are developed and there may be little or no clover; indeed in farming terminology there is no "bottom" to the sward, which is undesirable.

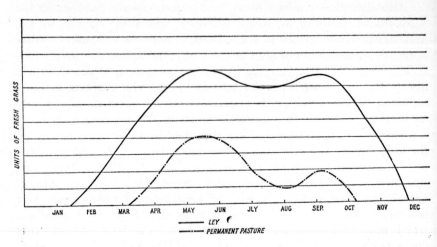

FIG 2.   GROWTH CURVES OF AVERAGE PERMANENT PASTURE COMPARED
WITH GOOD LEY IN DEVON

One essential difference between the cultivated permanent grass-lands and the uncultivated moors, downs, heaths and fens is a matter of fencing. The former are found in relatively small fenced units on which livestock can be controlled in their grazing, whereas the unfenced open grasslands may occupy hundreds or even thousands of acres. This permanent grassland may have been sown down or it may have "reverted" to grass during an agricultural depression; or perhaps, being an outlying field, it has been neglected until native species have taken complete hold on the land. Even where the land was originally sown years ago with a precise mixture it is unlikely that the sward to-day bears any relation to the mixture sown. The effects over many years, of grazing and fertilising, of soil and climate, will have changed the composition of the grassland community. Moreover, a character-istic feature of much permanent grassland is the high proportion of weeds which it is likely to contain—buttercups, dandelions, daisies, ribgrass and docks, to name a few.

The most productive permanent grassland contains a high propor-tion of the really useful grasses like perennial ryegrass, cocksfoot and timothy, with white clover. The more contaminated it is with weed species like bent, Yorkshire fog, and other inferior grasses, the lower

PLATE 3. Controlled grazing on a farm at Headley, Surrey. The grazing is rationed by means of an electric fencer

PLATE 4. Grasses at the water's edge, near the Cuillin hills on Skye — country devoted to rough grazing by hardy cattle and sheep

the productivity. Hence it is possible to assess the merit of a permanent pasture on, say, the amount of perennial ryegrass it contains. This method was actually adopted by Stapledon and Davies in their survey of the grassland of England and Wales carried out in 1938-40 and in the re-survey of the same sample areas conducted by the Grassland Research Institute in 1947 and again in 1959. Under their classification grassland was grouped as follows:

1. *First-grade ryegrass pasture*—containing 30 per cent or more perennial ryegrass with appreciable amounts of wild white clover, cocksfoot, timothy and other productive species.

2. *Second-grade ryegrass pasture*—containing 15 to 30 per cent perennial ryegrass with appreciable amounts of the other useful species.

3. *Third-grade ryegrass pasture*—with up to 15 per cent of this grass, the principal adulterant being bents.

4. *Agrostis pasture*—in which bent is the main constituent, with only small amounts of the better grasses and clovers.

Lower down the scale the pastures will contain increasing amounts of fescues, Nardus, Molinia and cotton grass, together with their usual associates, such as sedges, rushes, heather, bilberry and even scrub. The results of the survey based on this classification are given in the table on p. 36.

The striking and alarming lesson to be learnt from this survey is the small amount of really productive permanent pasture in the country as a whole. The first-class grazing pastures are noted for their quality. There are, for instance, the Welland Valley on the borders of Leicestershire, Rutland and Northamptonshire, and the eastern part of Romney Marsh. The soil here is extremely fertile, which confirms the fact—contrary to general opinion—that grass demands a high level of fertility in order to be fully productive. Closely approximating to these areas in excellence are the fattening pastures of the Midlands (mainly Leicestershire and Northamptonshire), parts of Cheshire and the Dee Valley, Blackmore Vale in Dorset, with the marshlands of Kent, Sussex, and Norfolk, the Bridgewater area of Somerset and the Exe Valley in Devon. Good permanent swards can also be seen in Berkshire and Wiltshire, the Lindsey division of Lincolnshire and the Monmouthshire "moors."

These well-known pastures are characteristically early in commencing growth in the spring and produce an abundance of herbage of high quality in May and June. This is due mainly to the fertility of the soil and the high content of perennial ryegrass, which is one of

G.G.   D

TABLE 5. ACREAGES AND PERCENTAGES OF DIFFERENT
TYPES COMPRISING THE PERMANENT GRASS AND ROUGH GRAZINGS OF
ENGLAND AND WALES (1938-40)

TYPE	Area in acres	Per cent
Permanent Pastures		
First-grade ryegrass pasture	251,000	1·2
Second-grade ryegrass pasture	912,000	4·4
Third-grade ryegrass pasture	4,317,000	20·2
Agrostis pasture including Agrostis-with-fescue, torgrass, etc.	9,580,000	45·0
Agrostis with rushes and sedges	734,000	3·4
Rough and Hill Grazings		
Fescue pasture, including the Down and Cotswold fescue swards	1,499,000	7·0
Areas of dense bracken fern	406,000	1·9
Areas of dense gorse	65,000	0·3
Areas of mixed fern and gorse (including those based on *Agrostis setacea* in Devon and Cornwall)	45,000	0·2
Nardus-fescue moor	292,000	1·4
Nardus-fescue with rushes	136,000	0·6
Molinia moor	176,000	0·9
Molinia-with-Nardus moor	866,000	4·1
Mixed Molinia, heather, fern and gorse moor (largely S.W. England)	106,000	0·5
Heather moor	794,000	3·7
Heather "fell"	361,000	1·7
Cotton grass and deer grass moor	414,000	1·9
Lowland heaths (New Forest type)	154,000	0·7 ⎫
Lowland heaths (Breckland type)	45,000	0·2 ⎭
Fen and "carr"	36,000	0·2
Estuarine saltings	57,000	0·3 ⎫
Sand dunes	31,000	0·1 ⎭
Lowland bog (not classified)	30,000	0·1
Field (Lowlands) invaded by tall thorn and scrub	12,000	less than 0·1
TOTAL PERMANENT PASTURE AND ROUGH GRAZINGS	21,319,000	100·0

our earliest spring grasses. They are capable of fattening prime bullocks and heifers without recourse to artificial feeding and give a sequence of growth throughout the grazing season, the normal stocking being one or more beasts per acre from April to July. As the cattle mature ready for slaughter, so more are drafted in for finishing; the output from the best fields is around 250 lb. of liveweight gain per acre per annum, and may reach as high as 300 to 500 lb. As might be expected considerable skill on the part of the grazier is required to keep these pastures at the peak of perfection. With the use of the mowing machine, and careful adjustment of the numbers of stock grazing to the growth of the grass, the swards are maintained like billiard tables. One never finds a grass in flower in these fields, for the grazier realises the folly of under stocking. He is aided in this by the fact that the grasses are inherently leafy, of the S.23 type, and produce large numbers of tillers at the base instead of running up flower stalks. This results in the production of the mid-season leafage which is so valuable to the grazier for finishing his cattle. This means, also, the necessity for regularly spreading the droppings which, if left untouched, produce coarse, tufted grass and give rise to uneven grazing. During the winter months it is usual to stock the land only with sheep and then only one to an acre, for cattle with their greater weight would damage the soft ground. When the grass is some four inches long, around mid-March to early April, the most forward cattle, in terms of condition, are turned into the pastures. As growth increases and approaches a peak, or "flush," towards the end of May or early June, so the numbers of stock are increased. The first cattle to commence grazing are likely to be fit for the butcher by mid-June, having put on some two hundredweight of liveweight.

The daily liveweight gain on the best pastures is of the order of 2·5 lb. per head for the full grazing period of ninety to one hundred days. The grazier always has cattle in reserve and here lies part of the secret of his success. By maintaining this reserve he can always adjust the number of mouths per acre to cope adequately with the growth of grass, whatever the season may be. The leafage is consumed at the peak of perfection, as if a mowing machine were used, and the production of more leafage from new side tillers is thus ensured. In fact it is said that each day's fill of grass should be grown the previous night.

The botanical analysis of a typical fattening pasture in the Market Harborough district of Leicestershire is as follows:

Perennial ryegrass	45 per cent ground cover
Cocksfoot	7
Rough-stalked meadow grass	15
Crested dogstail	7
White clover	25
Miscellaneous plants	1
	100

Finally, there are the sown pastures and meadows, which are called leys, leas, or layers. The distinguishing feature here is in the complete or almost complete freedom from weed species and the presence only of the sown, productive species of grasses. By reason of this purity of sward, the fields commence growth very early in the spring and continue to grow until late in the autumn. They give a high yield of nutritious herbage and recover rapidly from cutting or grazing. The ingress of weed species, both grasses and others, is always a likely eventuality. As the years go by, so the weed population tends to increase, and the productivity of the ley declines in consequence, until in the third or fourth year, depending upon the rotation followed, the system of farming practised, and the standard of husbandry, it may be ready to be ploughed up and cropped. Most leys, even with good management, if left down for ten years or so take on the characteristics of permanent grassland—and then not those of the best types, but more usually of the third or fourth grade. The longer growing season of a ley compared with that of permanent pasture and the greater productivity of the ley is clearly demonstrated in Fig. 2 on page 34.

CHAPTER 5

THE BREEDING OF GRASSES

It is not known who can claim to be the first British breeder of grasses, but William Marshall (1745-1818) was the first to expound the idea that populations of a particular grass species can show wide variations. Marshall had been a planter in the West Indies and later farmed in Surrey, but in addition he was a good agricultural botanist with a keen eye for observation. During the course of his work he had noted that while ryegrass persisted in the best feeding pastures, it died out within a year or two when sown in a ley. In his *Rural Economy of Gloucestershire* (1789), he records "How easy to collect the native species which abounds on the old grasslands and thus raise a new variety adapted on a certainty to the vale land ... and it only wants a little exertion." Marshall notes that one of the well-known agriculturalists of the day, William Pacey, had secured an indigenous form of perennial ryegrass in this way and was multiplying it up on his thousand-acre farm in Northleach. So well known did this strain of ryegrass become that by 1792 orders outstripped his supply and he secured half a guinea a bushel for this seed compared with the normal price of about half-a-crown. Unfortunately, this genuine indigenous ryegrass was later lost, and although it and other local selections, such as Devon Eaver, were used to some extent, their true importance was never generally understood, and the great bulk of the perennial ryegrass sown continued to be of the heavy-seeding, short-ley type which Marshall had rightly condemned.

Perennial ryegrass was the most popular grass until about 1831, although Loudon, the agricultural and horticultural encyclopædist, made the suggestion in 1828 that "New and excellent varieties of many of the grasses might no doubt be obtained by selection and cross breeding, and it was much to be wished that this should be attempted by cultivators."

A few years later Italian ryegrass took the stage and since it

satisfied the needs of the times there was little inducement for further
breeding work, and of course the depressed state of agriculture in those
days was not conducive to pioneer efforts.

In 1887, Robert Elliott, who returned to Scotland from being a
coffee planter in Mysore, embarked on a series of experiments on his
estate in Roxburghshire which were to have a far-reaching influence
on British agriculture. Taking in hand one of the poorest farms,
which was virtually derelict, he demonstrated in the course of the next
thirty years how the ley (i.e. a grass and clover mixture), properly
sown and well managed, was the guardian of soil fertility. He adopted
an eight-year rotation: roots; cereals; roots; cereals; four-year ley.
Following the ley, he grew a series of crops which exceeded in yield
arable crops grown in the normal fashion with fertiliser.

He laid down the following maxims for farmers:

(1) Success in farming depends on cutting production costs.

(2) The cheapest food for herbivorous animals is grass.

(3) The cheapest plant food for arable crops comes from good
grasses and deep-rooting plants.

(4) The cheapest and most successful cultivators of the soil, both
in draining and securing warm soil conditions, are the roots of grasses
and herbs.

The mixture listed opposite exemplifies the type Elliott sowed and
found so invaluable for his purpose of fertility replenishment.

To test out Elliott's mixture under contrasting conditions the School
of Agriculture, Cambridge, carried out trials from 1903 to 1905, and
exhibited turfs at meetings of the Royal Agricultural Society, to illustrate their excellent pasture-producing potential.

In about 1893 Dr. John Garton of Warrington, a founder of the
world famous firm which bears his name, carried out a good deal of
work on hybridisation. His method consisted of intercrossing species
and genera to produce the maximum number of "sports," and he was
the first to produce "perennialised Italian ryegrass" which was a cross
between perennial and Italian ryegrasses. This was the first bred
strain to be produced and marketed by a seed firm in this country
and the same technique has since been used by grass breeders in New
Zealand to produce their well known "short-rotation ryegrass" or
"H.I." ryegrass.

At the same time research into grasses was proceeding in the
United States, particularly with timothy which was in demand as horse
fodder. Clark, at Cornell in 1894, had 3,500 individual plants in his
breeding nursery and Hopkins of Virginia produced a number of

	lb.
Cocksfoot	10
Tall Oatgrass	3
Golden Oatgrass	$\frac{1}{2}$
Tall Fescue	4
Meadow Fescue	5
Hard Fescue	1
Rough-stalked Meadow Grass	$\frac{1}{2}$
Smooth-stalked Meadow Grass	1
Italian Ryegrass	3
Kidney Vetch	$2\frac{1}{2}$
Chicory	3
Burnet	8
Sheep's Parsley	1
Yarrow	$\frac{1}{2}$
Late-flowering Red Clover	2
White Clover	2
Alsike Clover	1
	48

improved strains. Experience indicated, however, that the strains evolved by various experimental stations and by breeders were not very adaptable to widely differing soil and climatic conditions and this lead to the dictum that the best results were secured by breeding from local plants adapted to specific conditions. The same conclusion was reached simultaneously by Swedish breeders under conditions where the differences in latitude are considerable.

The breeding of herbage plants on systematic lines first started in Europe at Svalöf, in Sweden, in 1904 and this plant breeding station has retained to this day a wonderful reputation for the quality of its work and the excellence of its products. It soon became clear from their work that the American experts were correct in their conclusions that wide variations existed within a simple species, not only in morphological characters, such as leaf size and height of plant, but also in physiological characters like earliness, drought resistance and winter hardiness. These wide variations offer to the plant breeder excellent opportunities for selection. At Svalöf, the work rapidly expanded from a study of timothy to cocksfoot, meadow and red fescues and perennial ryegrass.

The next milestone in the history of grass breeding was 1908, when the Danish State Trials included grasses and clovers for the first time. Unlike former trials, the yardstick selected was yield of hay per acre instead of yield of seed, a change of emphasis which was to have far-reaching results. Italian ryegrass, Tystofts 152, proved outstanding in these trials with the result that when seed was first made readily available in 1912 the entire stock, some 12 cwt. of seed, was sold to merchants and seed-growers' associations at 450 shillings per hundredweight. So excellent was this strain that it acquired what was virtually a monopoly in Denmark and retained its supremacy for many years. Even when it was ultimately replaced by new strains, these were derived from the old strain and were in fact only slightly superior to it.

Until the outbreak of war in 1914, farmers in this country depended very largely on foreign sources of seed for the commonly used herbage species in leys. Most of the ryegrass came from northern Ireland and Scotland, the broad red clover from south-eastern England, the cocksfoot and meadow fescue from Denmark, timothy from North America, and the so-called white Dutch clover from various European sources, while considerable importations of red clover were made from a wide range of countries.

The main consideration in selecting these (commercial) seeds was that of price, and quite naturally the producers of the seed propagated the best seed-producing types, rather than concentrating on those species giving the greatest amount of leaf. As a result, practically all the plants grown from these cheap imported seeds were short-lived, stemmy, and early to produce ear. When, therefore, they were included in mixtures intended to remain down for a number of years, they generally died out, and were replaced by poor quality volunteer grasses and weeds. In this way, sown leys rapidly deteriorated and the productivity and quality were much inferior to well-managed, permanent pastures. As a result of this experience, a strong body of opinion was created which considered permanent pastures preferable to leys and the production of a first-class pasture from arable land a matter requiring tremendous skill and a large amount of luck.

The failure of commercial seeds mixtures to produce long leys which would retain their productivity led to a study of the plant types growing in our best old pastures and it soon became evident that great variations existed in growth form. Broadly speaking, these indigenous species were leafier, more resistant to disease, had pronounced winter greenness and were more persistent, but at the same time were shy in producing seed.

With the foundation of the Welsh Plant Breeding Station at Aberystwyth in 1919, and the Scottish Society for Research in Plant Breeding in 1921, herbage plant breeding in this country began to make an impact on farming thought and planning.

At Aberystwyth, Sir George Stapledon and his staff began planting out large collections of indigenous plants for observation and for obtaining breeding material for the future. The outstanding plants for leafiness and winter greenness, for persistency and resistance to disease, for grazing, for mowing, for yield of herbage or for other characteristics were selected to form the parent material for a whole host of strains.

The work at Aberystwyth led to work at the Scottish Plant Breeding Station, the Plant Breeding Institute, Cambridge, and amongst private firms at home and abroad, and the very complicated business of selecting the right strain can be imagined from the description of the recognised strains of each species in Chapter 6.

More recently the breeding of new grasses has been added to the programme of the Plant Breeding Institute, Cambridge, which, situated in a low rainfall area in contrast to the Welsh Institute, acts as an excellent counterpart. Grasses produced at Aberystwyth under high rainfall conditions do not necessarily act in the same way when growing under the dry and often drought conditions of the eastern counties.

Apart from isolated cases of farmers growing crops of grass for seed for their own use, the supply has been the constant concern of seed specialists and importers. The second world war, when shortage of grass seed was acute, forced more farmers into the business of grass seed production and incidentally indicated to them the immense potential for an additional cash crop. In round figures about thirty thousand tons of grass seed of all types is required annually together with about ten thousand tons of clovers—no mean market.

As a result, nearly every county now has its herbage seed growers, for specialised equipment is not needed and as we have seen already the grass crop fits in well with most farming systems. What is more, grazing can still be obtained from the field as well as a seed crop and a useful additional source of income is thus secured, quite apart from avoiding overloading the cereal acreage which often results in the spread of diseases like eyespot and "take-all," and encourages the development of persistent weeds like wild oats.

A comprehensive national scheme for pedigree seed certification is now available, the products being marked as "British Certified

Herbage Seeds" bearing a guarantee as to purity, germination, and variety from the British Certifying Authority which is an official body composed of growers, seed trade members, research workers, and advisory officers. To-day a farmer is assured of an ample supply of seed of guaranteed quality at a competitive price.

When discussing the breeding of grasses a distinction must be made between "commercial" and "bred" strains.

As has already been said, "commercial" seed, such as the ryegrasses from Ireland and Scotland, the cocksfoot from Denmark and America, by reason of their being products of purely seed growing enterprises (in which individual plants were automatically selected for one character only, that of heavy seed production), were agriculturally inferior to the "bred" strains, or "S" strains as the Aberystwyth products were designated. Thus there came about a very clear distinction between "bred" strains and "commercial" strains, which came to apply also to clovers. Thus Montgomery late-flowering red clover, the wild white clover from Kent, Sussex and Hereford pastures, and the indigenous grasses like Devon Eaver and Kentish ryegrass became well known for their special qualities. Farmers became impressed with the fact that grasses such as ryegrass were not merely one species, but embraced a number of distinct strains, each with characteristic qualities of value to the farmer, such as earliness or lateness, leafiness, persistency, drought resistance, and so on.

This appreciation of the great variation in strains of grasses and clovers naturally had an immense impact on seed merchants who now seek to produce and sell better types of herbage seed, named in much the same manner as the seeds of our other farm crops. Incidentally, it is now more usual to use the term "variety" rather than "strain," but both words are used as synonyms.

It will be readily appreciated that many of these improved varieties selected for their capacity to produce stock food, i.e. herbage, in direct contrast to the old commercial types which were propagated and selected mainly on their capacity to produce seed, are relatively shy seeders. Each strain has a definite form or growth shape, growth rate and maturity date, which is usually expressed as the date when the inflorescence appears. This is variable. In the ryegrasses, for instance, the onset of maturity depends upon a minimum length of day (photoperiod). Without this, the plant does not flower but remains in the vegetative state. The necessary photoperiod varies greatly between the early strains and the late ones.

How does a plant breeder set about the task of developing a new strain or meeting some specific need in grassland farming? First, the need must be defined: for instance it may be for a grass especially early growing in spring, or one particularly resistant to drought, or perhaps one that fills a particularly lean gap in the normal grazing season in a certain district. He then determines that this need is likely best to be met by perennial ryegrass for example. Thousands of individual plants of perennial ryegrass are then collected from as wide a range of sources as possible and especially from populations subject to the particular hazard in mind, early grazing, drought or the like. These will be planted out as individuals and studied in detail, the worthless ones being discarded until ultimately comparatively few plants will remain which have stood up to the various tests and these will be used as parent material. These plants will then undergo some form of progeny testing, such as diallel crossing, where every individual plant is crossed with every other plant in the group, and the offspring carefully studied. Hand pollination, which is necessary in this work, is a very skilled job requiring infinite patience. The anthers are removed (emasculation) from a number of florets on one or more inflorescences of the plants which are to be used as female parents. Unemasculated florets are cut away, and each inflorescence is then covered with a semi-transparent, pollen-proof, paper bag. When the stigmas are exserted the bag is temporarily removed and they are pollinated by hand, the pollen previously collected from the plant selected as the male parent being brushed on to them. Hand pollination is a daily task since the pollen rapidly loses its viability and once flowering (anthesis) begins stigmas are exserted and the pollen is liberated daily for about a week.

Time of flowering itself varies appreciably with the species in a sequence which commences with timothy at the break of dawn, followed by cocksfoot and meadow fescue around 6 a.m. Perennial ryegrass is more leisurely and anthesis comes towards noon, while *Agrostis tenuis* is even later still, in the afternoon. By way of contrast, Yorkshire fog flowers twice a day, once at about 8 a.m. and again in the early afternoon. Weather conditions influence the occurrence of anthesis and for perennial ryegrass direct morning sunshine is essential, while for those species which flower very early in the morning, sunshine the previous evening is required.

To simplify the whole process and eliminate the tedium of hand pollination, a method known as "automatic pollination" was developed by Jenkin. This consists of placing the male or pollen-producing plant in the same paper bag as the emasculated female plant in such a way that the pollen at flowering time automatically falls on to the stigmas of the other parent.

A still further method of rapid multiplication, also developed at Aberystwyth, is known as the "polycross" system. Plants selected as parents are split up into vegetative pieces each containing an adequate amount of root to establish it as an individual plant. These "clones" are then planted out in the field in a randomised fashion in an area which can be adequately isolated by distance, preventing any contamination by pollen from other plants. Any cross fertilisation which takes place, therefore, is restricted to the plants within this area and the seed obtained is bulked. Progeny from this seed can then be compared for the characteristics which are required by the plant breeder. This method is much less time-consuming than hand pollination under greenhouse conditions and has the further great advantage that it does not require elaborate and costly equipment and is much more economical so far as technical labour is concerned. There is no one method superior in all circumstances to another, and each plant breeder uses the method or combination of methods best suited to his specific needs—the goal always being the same, namely to establish plants which can be used as parents to provide progeny still true to type, quality, and purpose in the third or fourth generations. With grasses, unlike many other plants, inbreeding has not proved generally successful, progeny usually showing loss of vigour and size. It is true, however, that some grasses display added vigour as a result of inbreeding, and workers in all the grass breeding countries use it as a method for academic purposes. It also provides a test of genetic purity (homozygosity) when needed.

Great efforts are being made by plant breeders to produce new plants synthetically by doubling the number of chromosomes in the species or in the hybrids obtained by inter-specific crossing. For this purpose the breeders use either the drug colchicine or doses of radiation. So far the results, however, have proved disappointing. Nevertheless, when Nature herself performs the operation the results are often strikingly successful, as for instance in the classic example of *Spartina* × *townsendii*. This cord-grass originated naturally on the mudflats of Southampton water and was discovered in 1870, near Hythe. The story is very interesting. *Spartina maritima* is our only indigenous cord-grass, but an American species, *S. alterniflora*, was found at Southampton in the early part of the nineteenth century and since *S.* × *townsendii* is intermediate in its morphological characters between these two it was thought to be a hybrid. However, it proved fertile and true-breeding, which gave cause for doubt. Later Huskins, working at the John Innes Horticultural Institute in 1930, showed that *S.* × *townsendii* had 126 chromosomes, whereas *S. maritima* possessed 56 and *S. alterniflora* 70. Now, if *S.* × *townsendii* had been a hybrid produced in the normal way, it would presumably have had 63 chromosomes, 28 from the one parent and 35 from the other. Huskins' theory was that this hybrid must have produced seed with double the number of chromosomes, i.e. 126, which, being an even number, would mean that the plants were fertile. This fertility enabled the plant to spread rapidly and Nature herself had provided the means by supplying widespread areas of moving mud flats where for centuries plants had been unable to grow; moreover, while the herbage of *Spartina* × *townsendii* is in no way comparable to such grasses as perennial ryegrass, cocksfoot or timothy, it is palatable and can be made into useful hay or silage.

The targets of research into grasses have been defined as: (1) increased yield, (2) good spring growth, (3) good aftermath following the hay crop, (4) production at a high level over the full life of the ley, (5) a high proportion of green-leaf to stem, (6) persistency of the strain. Any strain which adds to these characteristics the ability to produce late grazing in the autumn, and/or very early grazing in the spring, must commend itself to farmers in this country and in western Europe for the simple reason that this reduces the reliance which must be placed on hay for winter feeding. Even to-day, this is a crucial factor. Winter feeding is costly and any plant or any system of farming is eagerly sought after which enables cattle and sheep to secure their own food, growing *in situ*, beyond or before the normal grass growing season.

One additional factor is of paramount importance: the digestibility of the grasses produced. In the ruminant only a small proportion of the food which is "digested" is lost in the rumen gases and the bulk passes into the bloodstream to be used as a source of protein and energy. No farm food is completely digestible and in most cases a figure of 80 to 85 per cent digestibility is obtained. Clearly a grass which is 80 per cent digestible is more valuable than one with a digestibility of 60 per cent and in the latter case other factors such as earliness in spring or late growth in autumn or resistance to drought would be demanded if this particular grass were to be of value.

At the Grassland Research Institute the digestibility of grasses has for many years now been assessed by feeding them to sheep under controlled conditions. The digestibility of any food is that part which is not excreted and hence by collecting and analysing the fæces the digestibility of any specific grass can be obtained. Unfortunately this work is expensive, a large amount of the grass is required and each test takes a long time and hence in the past the amount of information obtained on this vital aspect of grass value has been very limited.

Recently a new laboratory method at the Grassland Research Institute has been perfected whereby one half gram of food only is required for test and the result can be obtained in five days. Good agreement has been secured between these purely laboratory tests (*in vitro*) and those carried out on live animals.

A small representative sample of the grass is dried and milled through an o·i mm. sieve. Half a gram of the dried sample is placed in a test tube with 40 ml. of artificial saliva and 10 ml. of rumen liquor from sheep fed wholly on a diet of hay. The tube is then filled with carbon dioxide and a valve fitted to permit the digestion gases to escape but exclude the entry of air. Digestion is allowed to proceed for forty-eight hours at body temperature, this simulating the action of the rumen. The undigested residue is then filtered off and a further forty-eight hours of digestion carried out, this time with 50 ml. of o·5 per cent pepsin solution to simulate the digestion in the lower gut. The final residue represents the undigested portion of the sample and by weighing, a figure for the digestibility of the grass is secured.

The speed and simplicity of this method allows a measurement to be made for the separate parts of the plant—leaf, leaf sheath and stem at different stages of growth—which is likely to prove invaluable as a guide to the management of a sward. The work has shown that when immature herbage is cut or grazed the true stem is more digestible than leaf or leaf sheath. As the plant reaches the flowering stage, however, and the stem contributes more to the bulk of the herbage so digestibility is markedly reduced. Formerly it was assumed that this low digestibility of the stem was a constant feature of grasses and hence plant breeders were at pains to produce leafy strains. In all probability, therefore, grasses have been discarded as of little feeding value when in fact, had they been utilised at an immature stage of growth, they might have proved exceptionally nutritious. The pattern of breeding in the future may therefore change, now that it is possible to concentrate on the improvement of quality as well as that of seasonal productivity.

The use of controlled climate cabinets enables physiological studies to be carried out on the many progenies of a breeding programme. An ingenious device constructed at the Cambridge Plant Breeding Institute allows the foliage to be exposed to −16° C while the soil temperature is nearer to that of winter conditions, the soil in winter being usually much warmer than the air temperature.

At Cambridge three cocksfoot synthetics and two synthetics of tall fescue are showing decided promise in meeting herbage needs where gaps now exist in the seasonal pattern of production. The new Aberystwyth cocksfoot, S.345, just available, should provide earlier fodder than is at present possible from this grass, while S.352 timothy is likely to give heavier crops for hay or silage. The efforts of our plant breeders must influence our grassland management techniques very considerably in the near future.

Under modern conditions, therefore, the growing of grass is no longer a haphazard affair. On the other hand it is not just a matter for the specialists. To counteract the higher prices which research, and especially the low seeding capacity of modern grasses, inevitably cause, the new strains must be grown scientifically, and as crops in their own right, which means an extra cash crop for the farmer.

An added inducement to plant breeders came in 1964, when the Plant Varieties and Seeds Act became law. Royalties can now be collected on the commercial use of approved varieties of wheat, barley and oats and perhaps in time this will be possible for grasses also.

CHAPTER 6

THE CONSTITUENTS OF GRASSLAND

There are about ten thousand known species of grasses, some 150 to 160 in the British Isles. Few of these, however, are of agricultural importance and only about ten are regularly sown. This number is increased if one includes lawns and playing fields, for farm and recreation have quite different requirements.

Possibly the earliest grass to be cultivated in Britain was perennial ryegrass, which was often called ray grass. Perennial ryegrass is indigenous to fertile soils, not only in this country but in Europe and Asia as well, and needs good, deep soil to succeed, for on light land and in dry districts or seasons it tends to die out. It is one of the most palatable grasses and this, combined with its long growing season, its ready response to either cutting or grazing, and its perennial character, makes it our most valuable grass. It forms the basis of most mixtures for both long and short leys and being easy to establish it produces a good yield of herbage the first year after seeding. The maximum production of herbage is attained in the second year. As one might well expect, it is unusual to find perennial ryegrass on moorlands and upland pasture. It is interesting to note in passing that a member of the same genus, darnel (*Lolium temulentum*), is a weed which can be poisonous to stock and is believed to be the "tares" referred to in the Bible.

Italian ryegrass, unlike perennial ryegrass, is not indigenous to Britain, but is widely grown throughout the British Isles. The nutritive value and palatability is high and it is a very productive grass, particularly in early spring and autumn. Growth is earlier than perennial ryegrass, it flowers in May or early June, and this characteristic, combined with its ready establishment from seeding, means that it is particularly suitable for producing an early spring bite and for catch cropping, the practice of slipping in a quick growing crop between

PLATE 5. Roadside verges form an important habitat for many grass species. Nowadays they are far too often cut down or poisoned with chemical sprays. This is the Lambourn valley in Berkshire

PLATE 6. *Left*, plants selected for their promise in the field growing in the greenhouse for seed production

Right, the seed obtained from these plants growing in observation plots in the trial grounds

two crops in a rotation, to obtain additional growth. To take an example, early potatoes will be lifted in June and the ground may not be required until the next crop, which is often wheat, is sown in autumn. Immediately after the potatoes are lifted, therefore, Italian ryegrass can be sown at about 30 to 40 lb. per acre and, within six weeks of sowing, cattle or sheep will be grazing. Some six weeks of cheap grazing can thus be obtained, largely because of the easy establishment and rapid growth of this valuable grass. It persists for two years only and is sometimes used as a nurse crop when sowing land down to a much longer ley.

How can one distinguish between these two common grasses in the field? Italian ryegrass is generally earlier in growth and its spikelets, each made up of 5 to 15 florets alternating in two rows on the rachis, are awned, unlike perennial ryegrass. In both species the leaf blades are dark green, glossy below and dull above, and distinctly ribbed, but whereas in Italian ryegrass the leaf blades are rolled in the shoot, in perennial ryegrass they are folded. The leaf sheath in both cases is glabrous with a reddish coloration.

Commercial supplies of seed of Italian ryegrass come from Denmark, France, Ireland, Ayrshire and New Zealand. These are mostly early and high yielding but slightly less persistent than the bred strains. Westerwolds or Express ryegrass is an annual form of Italian, giving most of its growth in the first six months after sowing. This form comes from Holland and there are a number of named strains which are more persistent and leafy than the commercial seed. Aberystwyth S.22 Italian ryegrass is leafier than commercial strains, rather later in heading but more persistent, and provides good growth over two years. A cross between Italian and perennial ryegrass, emanating from New Zealand and known as Short Rotation ryegrass (H.1), will persist for three to four years on fertile soils but lacks winter hardiness under some conditions.

The strains of perennial ryegrass are divided broadly into three groups, Early, Intermediate and Late, according to time of flowering and commencement of growth in spring. The majority of strains used for hay are in the early group while the late group is noted for leaf, high tillering capacity and persistency.

The early group includes Aberystwyth S.24, Devon Eaver and commercial seed from Ayrshire, New Zealand and Northern Ireland. The intermediate group contains Aberystwyth S.101, Danish and Kentish seed, while by far the best known and used strain in the later group is Aberystwyth S.23.

A new strain of perennial ryegrass, Aberystwyth S.321, became available for the first time in 1965 and this has been bred specifically for high resistance to autumn and winter burn. By burn is meant the yellowing and scorching of the grass with frost and cold dry winds which makes the grass unpalatable and hence reduces its usefulness at a time of year when grass is very valuable.

Cocksfoot, a long-lived perennial, is indigenous to Europe, Asia, and Africa, and produces more bulk than any other of our grasses. In Britain it is most frequently found on heavy, fertile soils in lowland areas. It commences growth early in spring, though not quite so early as perennial ryegrass, and flowers in May and June. The young shoots are particularly palatable and at this stage are very sensitive to management, so that care must be taken not to over graze when in this condition. Should this practice be repeated for a number of years, the plant dies out. On the other hand, when the plant is growing luxuriantly in July, August and September, equal care must be taken not to under stock, or the foliage becomes harsh and unpalatable, and soon rough, coarse tufts of uneaten herbage dominate the sward, so that it is known as a "very good friend but a bad master." The foliage is burnt by frost and hence should be eaten down before the onset of winter. The care necessary in management does not mean that this is a difficult grass to handle, and with the right treatment—proper grazing on the "on" and "off" basis—it has immense value, and, because of its high yield, is greatly prized for mowing hay or silage. The hay types, however, are not good grazing types. It is an excellent drought resister and will do well on light land where perennial ryegrass would quickly dry out in the summer months.

The inflorescence is readily recognised and is well named "cocksfoot." Equally easy to distinguish is the vegetative stage, for it is coarse and densely tufted and the leaves are light green in colour, almost whitish near the base, with rough edges. If one draws a blade of cocksfoot through the fingers the roughness is easily perceptible, and the fingers may even be cut. The leaf blades are folded in the shoot, ribless above, pointed, and have a very marked keel below; there is a long, membranous and very conspicuous ligule.

Most of the cocksfoot grown in this country used to come from Denmark and America and this commercial type is essentially a hay strain, which under hard grazing conditions tends to die out after a few years. If, however, it is grown on fertile land and is subject to reasonable grazing management, being rested at the proper intervals in the season, it can persist for many years. The American type is inferior to the Danish, being much more stemmy. The development of the true grazing strains of cocksfoot has been principally the work of the Plant Breeding Station, Aberystwyth, and it is to Aberystwyth that credit must be given for bringing to the notice of farmers the essential difference between the hay and pasture strains.

At one time cocksfoot was unpopular owing to its tremendous growth which, as we have already noted, becomes coarse and very unsightly if uncontrolled. To-day, however, it is regarded as one of the most valuable species in seeds mixtures, although under certain circumstances the herbage may be of lower digestibility.

The strains of cocksfoot available also fall into early, intermediate and late groups. Various Danish and American strains, together with Scotia, bred by the Scottish Society for Research in Plant Breeding, are early, with New Zealand Akaroa and Aberystwyth S.37 intermediate in type. The most widely used late strains are perhaps the Aberystwyth S.26 and S.143. A new strain from Aberystwyth, S.345, which is exceptionally early in the spring and makes appreciably more growth during milder spells in winter compared with Danish commercial types and S.37 was first marketed in 1965. It is, however, liable to winter burning.

Another of our most valuable grasses is timothy. It was recorded in New Hampshire in the seventeenth century and introduced in 1720 to Maryland by a certain Timothy Hansen. It quickly proved its worth as a hay-producing species and subsequently seeds were sent to England in 1760 under the name of "timothy," thus preserving the memory of its American sponsor. Since those days importations of timothy from America have taken place each year.

It is a late grass, giving heavy yields of leafy hay and it does particularly well on peaty soils in regions of high rainfall and low-lying, moist heavy land. It is often known as "cat's tail" which aptly describes the inflorescence. It is found growing indigenously in many parts of the country and a dwarf-growing prostrate type is native to the downlands. It has acquired wide popularity both for hay and grazing, being very palatable. It is winter-hardy and since it is late in producing flower heads it maintains its quality for a long period during the grazing season.

The flower heads as already indicated are easily recognised in the field, appearing in July and August. The leaf blades are rolled in the shoot, light green in colour and have a decidedly sweet taste. There are no auricles but a prominent, white membranous ligule.

Commercial seed comes from America, Canada and Scotland.

Superior strains are Omnia from Sweden and Scotia from the Scottish Plant Breeding Station and from Aberystwyth, S.48, S.50 and S.51. A new strain, S.352, well suited for the production of heavy, leafy crops for silage or hay was introduced in 1965.

Timothy offers excellent examples of how selected plants from old pastures have been used to build up new and recognisable strains. The original plants for Aberystwyth S.48, for instance, came from wild plants collected from a very old Dorset pasture, while cuttings taken from old pastures in the Midlands and Kent formed the parent material for Aberystwyth S.50 which is now classified as a separate species, *Phleum bertolonii*.

Meadow fescue, like timothy, does not compete well with heavy seedings of the ryegrasses, but harmonises with timothy and is frequently sown with this grass, in special mixtures for hay and late grazing. It is indigenous to Europe, Asia, and North America and does well on rich, heavy clays; it supplies excellent pasture in July and August, normally lean months on the farm, for the ryegrass usually produces very little growth at this time of year. Commercial strains of seed are mainly of Danish or American origin, but a number of bred strains are available, notably Aberystwyth S.215, which is a hay-pasture strain, and Aberystwyth S.53, which is a pasture strain. Palatability markedly decreases with age.

The panicles appear in June and July. The basal sheaths are reddish and there may be some confusion with the ryegrasses, especially as the leaves are dark green, ribbed above, with a glossy, smooth lower surface. The leaves are keeled, however, their edges are harsh, and when they are held up to the light distinct white, longitudinal lines are seen.

While the foregoing constitutes the common grasses to be used in seeds mixtures for the establishment of leys or permanent pasture, there are a number of other valuable grass species which, though they establish themselves slowly, are of use for very long leys or for sowing land away to permanent pasture. Amongst such grasses come rough and smooth-stalked meadow grasses, crested dogstail, meadow foxtail, and tall fescue (*Festuca arundinacea*). The latter has become well known only of recent years, largely because of its high yield of herbage and its marked growth in late autumn and very early spring. The development of this grass is, therefore, of the utmost importance in filling the "winter gap" in grass growth. Recent expeditions have been made to North Africa to secure suitable parent material for developing new strains, and accessions from Algeria, France, Norway, Morocco and Tunisia have been secured by the Plant Breeding Institute, Cambridge.

Rough and smooth-stalked meadow grasses are fairly comparable, being productive on rich soils, the foliage palatable and of high nutritive value, smooth-stalked being generally accepted as the inferior of the two. They are known as essentially bottom grasses because they are low growing and form a dense turf. For this very reason many farmers omit them from their seeds mixtures since, if the meadow grasses are not kept strictly within bounds, they have a decided tendency to squeeze out the more productive perennial ryegrass and timothy. Broadly speaking, rough-stalked meadow grass should be used on rich moist land, while smooth-stalked meadow grass revels in somewhat drier soil conditions. The latter is often used for hard-wearing lawns.

Smooth-stalked meadow grass is the more widely distributed, being indigenous to Europe, Asia and North America, and from the Mediterranean to the Arctic Circle, whereas its companion grass is restricted to Europe, Central Asia and America. Smooth-stalked meadow grass flowers in May to early July and rough-stalked in June to July.

Crested dogstail is indigenous to Europe, Asia and America. The one-sided panicles, which closely resemble a dog's tail, appear in June and July and since the stems are very tough and wiry they are unpalatable to stock and can be seen right through the autumn like stiff tooth-brushes standing about a foot high. Because of this feature the grass is a prolific self-seeder and given the opportunity may soon be the dominant species in the sward. It is most productive late in the season, is very winter green, and certainly has a value for poor upland pastures and poor dry soils.

Meadow foxtail is one of the earliest grasses to commence growth in the spring and also to flower. The inflorescence is readily identified, being a cylindrical, spike-like panicle, fairly compact and soft, resembling a fox's tail. The grass is indigenous to the temperate and colder regions and in Britain is commonly found on rich, fertile, heavy soils. Both nutritive value and palatability are high but the seed is expensive and difficult to establish, and is not normally recommended for inclusion in seeds mixtures.

It is usual to include one or more of the clovers in association with grasses. Being leguminous, clovers utilise the nitrogen of the atmosphere and when the root residues are mixed with the soil, nitrogen is subsequently released for the use of other plants. Moreover, the low-growing herbage of the clovers helps to knit the sward together and since the clovers are richer in protein over a longer period of the season than the grasses, the inclusion of these species improves the feeding value of the herbage. It is important, however, not to have too high a clover content in a sward, because this would give rise to dietary problems in the feeding of the stock. Besides, since clover is late in commencing growth in the spring time, a shortage of keep would be inevitable in the early part of the year, which is the crucial time on many dairy and stock farms. Finally, the bulk of herbage produced by the clovers is lower than is the case with many of our grasses. We have come, therefore, to regard the clovers as complementary to the grasses and not as their competitors.

The two most important clover species are red and white. In the former are included broad-leaved or early red clovers. Much of the seed is English grown, Dorset Marl being an excellent example, while the imported varieties come from Canada, New Zealand and France. Aberystwyth S.151 is a bred strain which is more leafy and shows greater persistency than the other types. Late-flowering red clover is more persistent than broad red clover, but is essentially a hay plant, though contributing to the grazing sward in the second year. Montgomery and Cornish Marl late-flowering red clovers are excellent strains, whilst Aberystwyth S.123 is based on some forty families derived from selected plants of Montgomery Red and Cornish Marl. In general therefore, the broad red clovers are used for hay and grazing leys of one year duration; late-flowering red clovers are used in leys of up to four years' duration.

Of the white clovers (*Trifolium repens*), there is a distinction between large white clover and wild white clover, the latter being considered an essential ingredient of all mixtures for three-year leys or longer. The large white clovers are generally more bulky than the wild white, but are shorter-lived and are included in leys for one or two-year grazing, principally by sheep. Holland supplies some of our seed and also New Zealand, while a very large-leafed variety called Ladino is imported from the United States. Aberystwyth S.100 has ousted most of our other strains of large white clover, since it is more persistent, giving good growth in the fourth year, begins growth earlier in the spring, and produces excellent seed crops. Of the wild white clovers, Kentish is possibly the most important and the best known, although Aberystwyth S.184 shows greater uniformity and can be regarded as an important type.

A number of other plants find their way into pastures and meadows, though seldom sown nowadays. Black medick (*Medicago lupulina*) for instance, is a short-lived clover-like plant which comes away quickly from sowing and flourishes on calcareous soils and in relatively dry conditions. It is a very ready self-seeder and should therefore always be grazed before it sets seed or it may have a smothering effect on other species. Most of our seed requirements are met from home-grown supplies. Generally speaking, however, the true clovers give much more bulk and if conditions are suitable, should be preferred.

Crimson clover (*Trifolium incarnatum*) is used as a catch crop, being very quick-growing and in association with Italian ryegrass it can be sown in August after harvesting the corn crop, particularly in the southern half of England. It makes no growth over the winter but, growing away rapidly in the spring, it provides early keep for stock and still leaves time for the land to be ploughed and cropped in the same season.

Kidney vetch (*Anthyllis vulneraria*) used to be sown in mixtures for sheep during the autumn or spring. It requires an adequate supply of lime in the soil and is not usually long-lived.

Lucerne (*Medicago sativa*), known in America by the Arabic name, alfalfa, is seldom sown in seeds mixtures and it is more common to grow the crop alone or with a single companion plant, such as cocksfoot, timothy, or meadow fescue. With its drought-resisting qualities it is particularly valuable for dry regions. Although grown extensively in the United States, New Zealand and Australia, it has never achieved the same success in this country, because it is difficult to establish. In our higher rainfall and more humid conditions it tends to be smothered by weeds or volunteer grasses in the first year. In the eastern half of England, however, provided the necessary attention is given to its manurial requirements and the land is clean, it does extremely well and will hold the ground for several seasons. On land which has not grown lucerne before it is very important to inoculate the seed with the appropriate root nodule "culture". This is purchased with the seed and the simple process of inoculation is carried out by wetting the seed with the culture diluted in separated milk. Our supplies of seed come chiefly from France and a number of strains are on the market.

Sainfoin (*Onobrychis viciifolia*), also known as St. Foin, cock's head, or holy grass, possesses excellent drought-resisting qualities; it does well on calcareous soils and is indeed indigenous to these soils in southern England. It is essentially a hay plant and there are two varieties—

giant, which is short-lived, but yields two crops of hay a year, and common which holds the ground for a number of years but only gives one cut of hay each year. The seed of the giant strains was originally introduced from France. Several strains of giant and common sainfoin seed, such as Cotswold sainfoin, are produced in this country.

In many of our best feeding pastures a considerable number of other edible herbs are found, and observation has established the fact that many of these plants are extremely palatable to stock and have good drought-resisting qualities. Chemical analysis indicates that they are very rich in minerals and many farmers believe that they have an intrinsic value and consequently sow a small amount of ribgrass, burnet, yarrow and chicory in their seeds mixtures. Others, instead of including them in the seeds mixtures, may sow what is termed a "herb strip" across their leys, and when this is done it is very evident that the stock relish these plants because the herb strip is invariably kept well grazed. Fields are not sown exclusively with these species because their cropping capacity does not compare with that of our more valuable grasses. It is interesting to note, however, that hay made from meadows including a large number of these herbs is always relished by stock and especially by sick animals, which may refuse otherwise good quality hay.

When land is sown down to grass, be it for grazing, hay or general usage, the problem arises of selecting the appropriate species and strains and of composing the seeds mixture.

At the beginning of the century very complex mixtures were used, probably because the farmers of those days were neither familiar with the merits and demerits of the different species nor informed on the question of fertilisers or the subsequent management of the sward. There was a general belief that if a large number of species were included in a mixture then at least some of them might succeed and ultimately produce a turf. This doubtless influenced Elliott in the choice of his mixture outlined in the previous chapter and comparable mixtures were used until the early part of this century when farmers became more critical of seeds and mixtures in general.

Trials carried out in the early 1930's, especially by Professor Gilchrist at Cockle Park, the University of Durham's experimental farm, indicated that such hit and miss methods were unnecessary and indeed undesirable. As a result of this work, the Cockle Park mixture was devised for sowing down land to a three-year ley or permanent sward, this being:

	lb. per acre
Perennial ryegrass	16
Cocksfoot	10
Timothy	4
Late flowering red clover	4
Alsike clover	1
Wild white clover	1
	36

The strains of the grasses and clovers used were usually common commercial ones obtained through the seed trade, although a few pioneer farmers did, in fact, collect and even breed their own seeds. So the permanent ryegrass was generally obtained from Ireland or Ayrshire, the cocksfoot from Denmark or North America and the timothy from Canada. This mixture is still used to-day, although with improved techniques of cultivation and greatly increased knowledge of fertilising, a lower seed rate—costing less—can safely be used. Moreover, the opportunity is generally taken to include at least a proportion of the "bred" strains of grasses and clovers to take advantage of their known improved qualities.

A mixture which has been used extensively is:

	lb. per acre
Perennial ryegrass (Irish or Danish)	4
Perennial ryegrass (Aberystwyth S.23)	4
Perennial ryegrass (Kent)	4
Cocksfoot (Danish)	4
Cocksfoot (Aberystwyth S.26)	4
Timothy (Canadian)	2
Timothy (Aberystwyth S.48)	2
Late-flowering red clover (Montgomery)	2
White clover (Aberystwyth S.100)	2
Wild white clover (Kent)	1
	29

Even so, there is a considerable body of opinion which regards the Cockle Park type of mixture as too complicated and many farmers now sow a mixture which contains but one grass and one clover. The reasoning in this case is that the grass selected is known by experience to succeed under the specific conditions on the farm and the clover is added to give balance. If additional needs must be met then other mixtures, equally simple in composition, are used in other fields. Thus in many cases a farm may be dotted with a number of ultra-simple mixtures in contrast to the farm of yesteryear which was sown with one, or at the most two, more complex mixtures which had to meet all the needs of the stock for grazing in summer and fodder in the winter. In practice one generally finds that the majority of farmers nowadays seek a solution to the problem in a compromise between over-complexity and ultra-simplicity.

CHAPTER 7

SEED PRODUCTION AND TESTING

For many farmers, herbage seed production now offers an alternative sales crop to cereals and enables them to extend the rotation, and to control diseases and pests which follow in the wake of too-intensive cereal cropping. To quote an example, a crop of cocksfoot yielded 500 lb. of seed per acre which was sold to a merchant for 2s. a pound, thus giving a gross return of £50 per acre and a good margin of profit, quite apart from some grazing before and after the seed crop was taken. Under favourable conditions this field is likely to yield a comparable harvest for another three years or perhaps longer.

Species and strains which are well suited to the soil and climatic conditions of a particular farm should be selected when a farmer intends to embark on grass seed production as an enterprise. The grassland policy will then rotate around these seed-producing types to ensure that pollination problems are minimised or eliminated and that seeds left in the soil or carried round the farm in the dung or fodder which is produced are not likely to affect the purity of the strain. Care must even be taken to ensure that seeds are not blown into a field from a passing wagon. Equally important is it for the farmer to secure a contract with a seedsman who will take his seed and thus ensure a market for what is a very specialised crop.

The procedure for contracting for growing herbage seed crops is usually as follows. The firm or society or association determines the acreage of any particular species or strain to be grown and assures itself that the farmer is a reliable person for the purpose. The fields in which it is proposed to grow the crop are inspected by a technical officer of the firm or organisation who, if he approves, counter-signs the appropriate application for stock seed. Stock seed is supplied to contract growers only and in due course the crop is inspected and certified.

No special equipment is required and the cultivation follows quite a normal pattern. Good land of high fertility must be selected. Every effort should be made to get the land free from weeds, and fertilising must be carried out with lime, phosphate, potash, and nitrogen, according to the type of soil and the herbage crop to be sown. Often the grass is sown under a cereal nurse crop along traditional rotational lines. The seed may be broadcast in some cases, while in others it is drilled in rows to enable inter-row hoeings to be carried out each year and thus help to keep weeds in check. Inter-drill cultivations must not under any circumstances be deep, however, for the feeding roots of the grasses, as we saw when discussing the structure of the grass plant, are in the main peripheral and hence easily damaged. To cut off the supply of nutrients to the plant means a reduced yield of seed.

"Rogueing" is another practice used to maintain the purity of a crop. The "rogues" or intruding plants of, for example, Yorkshire fog, with their characteristic grey-green woolly appearance, stand out during the winter months in pure stands of ryegrass, cocksfoot or timothy and can easily be spudded or hoed out. Other rogues, such as early strains of grasses in a crop of a particularly late strain, are readily observable in late spring and can be eliminated in a similar fashion.

In the spring a farmer must use his judgment as to when to shut the field up for seed production, for seasonal and local conditions vary widely. Ryegrass is often grazed lightly until March, for instance, whereas cocksfoot and timothy are usually left alone. Once shut up, the field is left as it would be were a cereal crop like wheat or barley being grown.

Skill is needed in deciding when to harvest the crop. Each species has its own characteristic signs of ripeness. The seed heads of the ryegrass for instance turn brown and resemble a hare's back, while the straw is yellowish to yellow-brown in colour. Cocksfoot heads are ready for cutting when grey-white. The usual test is to draw the seed heads gently through the palm of one's hand. If the crop is ripe, some seeds will be left in the hand. The ripeness of meadow fescue is much more difficult to judge, for the straw is frequently still green in the leafy strains when the seed is quite ripe. The seed heads will be greenish-brown. If left too late very considerable shedding of seed and consequent loss of crop will result. Years of experience are necessary to determine the correct stage of ripeness for cutting, and even then some losses through shedding must be expected. Fortunately the majority of grasses are ripe for harvest between hay and silage making on the one hand and the corn harvest on the other and this is a great advantage so far as the distribution of labour is concerned.

In the early days the traditional method of harvesting the grasses was to cut with a mower and to tie by hand into small sheaves as one did with cereals. The sheaves were stooked just like corn until nearly dry and then built into small mows or cocks in the field to dry out ready for carting. Later, farmers used a binder instead of a mower, and this continued until the advent of the combine-harvester. To-day, the combine, suitably adjusted for dealing with these very small seeds, is used on most farms. With a binder, the crop is cut in the early morning or late evening when it is damp with dew and the shedding of seed is then less likely. For the combine the crop must be completely ripe and absolutely dry and free from dew. There is a danger, however, that if high winds or a storm should arise when the seed is in this completely ripe condition a great quantity of seed will be shaken out and lost on the ground. The combine offers great flexibility and its use has unquestionably eased the problems of growing this tricky crop. With a pick-up attachment, for instance, it is capable of dealing with crops which have been flattened by winds and which, until the advent of the combine, had to be written off as a complete loss. Another advantage it offers is that grasses with long straw, such as cocksfoot or timothy, can be cut near the seed head and so most of the straw can be left in the field where it can later be grazed by cattle or, if not required, burnt over.

Another development of recent years is the introduction of artificial drying. The ideal method is considered to be to use the binder and cart the sheaves immediately to a barn hay-drier and drive off the surplus moisture until the sheaves are perfectly fit for stacking. This obviates the need for stooking in the field and, even more important, eliminates the risk of bad weather harming the crop. Once safely in the stack, the crop can mature naturally until it is finally threshed with a stationary threshing box.

A crop which is put into sheaves or stacked in loose conditions must be dry to the point of crackling before it is carted. Quite often, particularly in poor seasons, the stacks are built long and narrow to allow the wind to blow through them and help in the drying process. Chimneys made with sacks of straw drawn up through the stack as building proceeds help this drying-out process and prevent fermentation or heating in the stack. Heating must be prevented at all costs because of the adverse effect on seed germination.

In some districts bundles of faggots or layers of straw are built

into the stack for the same purpose. Invariably sheets are placed over
the bed of the wagons or carts used for transport to collect up any
seed which is threshed out automatically by the handling involved in
transport and would otherwise be lost.

Many of the snags outlined above can be overcome by double
combining, a practice which has been used very successfully in the
eastern counties. Cutting commences before the crop is completely
ripe at the stage when it would be necessary to leave it in the windrow
or swathe to dry out. A low cylinder speed is used with a wide setting
of the concave and this arrangement secures all the mature seeds
without damage. The straw is left in windrows by fitting deflector
plates and is allowed to remain there and mature. Then the combine,
with pick-up attachment and a normal setting of the drum and the
concave, is put into the crop and garners the rest of the seed.

The following table gives the yields of seed from various grasses
when grown on good land under good management:

TABLE 6. YIELDS OF MACHINE-DRESSED SEED

| Species | Strain | Yield in lb. per acre of cleaned seed | |
		Average yields (approx.)	Maximum yields recorded in Britain (approximate)
Perennial ryegrass	S.24	600	1,350
Perennial ryegrass	S.101	350	850
Perennial ryegrass	S.23	350	1,200
Cocksfoot	S.37	450	1,300
Cocksfoot	S.26	450	1,300
Cocksfoot	S.143	450	1,300
Timothy	S.51	300	800
Timothy	S.48	250	1,000
Timothy	S.50	200	500
Meadow fescue	S.215	300	840
Meadow fescue	S.53	200	800
Red fescue	S.59	300	850
Italian ryegrass	S.22	600	1,700

When a farmer purchases seed from his merchant he needs assur-
ances as to the quality of purity, germination and trueness to type.
Equally the merchant, when purchasing his stocks from the grower,
needs to know the quality in order to fix the price. The principles
underlying the assessment of seed quality by specific tests were

established about a hundred years ago. Techniques have since been developed to meet the ever-increasing demand for high quality seeds. Seed-testing under the Seeds Act 1920 is undertaken at the official Seed Testing Stations. Minor amendments were made by the Seeds (Amendment) Act, 1925, and the Agriculture (Miscellaneous Provisions) Act, 1954, but these did not seriously affect the chief principles of the main Act. The station at Cambridge which forms part of the National Institute of Agricultural Botany, covers England and Wales: there are separate stations for Scotland and Northern Ireland. The larger seed firms, who have of course very numerous samples which require testing, maintain their own private seed-testing stations. These are subject to close control, and check samples, tested at the official stations, ensure uniformity of results.

To secure the necessary information for the purpose of guaranteeing quality a representative sample of the seed must first be procured from the bulk supply. To obtain this sample seed must be obtained from the top, middle and bottom of each container. A "stick" sampler which is inserted at the top of the container must be divided into separate compartments. "Spear" samplers are also available which can be thrust into containers but, again, a sample extending from the middle to the outside of the container must be withdrawn. From this sample, purity, weed contamination and germination can be determined. Purity is expressed as the percentage by weight of the sample which consists of the genuine seed. A check is kept on weed seeds, and hence on the possible contamination of clean land, by recording the total percentage by weight of weed seeds, and (under new regulations) the actual number of seeds per sample of certain specially important weeds, scheduled as "Injurious Weed Seeds." These are dodder, docks and sorrels, wild oats, black grass, and couch grass.

A figure for germination indicates how much of the seed sown is likely to produce mature plants. If the germination factor is low, then in order to obtain the necessary number of plants in the field the farmer would need to sow a correspondingly larger amount of seed per acre. The germination tests are made in the laboratory by subjecting a unit number of seeds to controlled conditions of moisture supply and temperature. These conditions are designed to give the most regular, rapid and complete germination for the general run of samples likely to be obtained from a particular crop. Ideally, the seed should be tested under field conditions but it is impossible to ensure uniformity. Quite apart from statutory tests, seed health can be assessed by growing and identifying any disease organisms carried on the seed. The moisture content of seeds is a critical factor when periods of storage are involved. Progressive deterioration occurs above a certain moisture and can be prevented only by artificial drying. Seed is frequently carried over from one season to the next and provided it is stored in a dry, airy place free from vermin, in a cool, uniform temperature, it is perfectly safe to do this. Seed which is kept at low temperatures at or around freezing point stores satisfactorily without any appreciable loss of germination for many years.

PLATE 7. *Above left*, crested dogstail grass (*Cynosurus cristatus*). *Above right*, Timothy grass (*Phleum pratense*). *Below left*, cocksfoot grass (*Dactylis glomerata*). *Below right*, rough-stalked meadow grass (*Poa trivialis*)

PLATE 8. The River Fleet at Cookham, with some of the many grass species requiring abundant supplies of water

CHAPTER 8

WEEDS IN GRASSLANDS

The crucial factor in determining whether or not a particular plant is regarded as a grassland weed is agricultural merit. Since this is not always easy to assess, views as to whether a certain plant is a weed or not will vary, not only from place to place but also from time to time. Forty years ago, a seeds mixture for sowing down to a long ley or permanent pasture would probably include some thirty different species, many now regarded by farmers as weeds.

Let us take a simple example. A four-year ley mixture composed of perennial ryegrass, cocksfoot, timothy and white clover is sown on reasonably clean land. Within two years it can be assumed with fair certainty that one would find, on examination, established specimens of Yorkshire fog and bent. Under these conditions they would be classified as weeds and the farmer would make every effort to exterminate them in the knowledge that, being inferior grasses so far as productivity and palatability are concerned, the value of the ley is reduced in proportion to the degree of contamination. A hill farmer, on the other hand, used to heather, bilberry, gorse and bracken as intruders in his pasture, would place Yorkshire fog and bent in a very different category. So one can assume that most grasses are desirable in one type of grassland or another. We have also seen how certain broad-leaved plants like chicory (*Cichorium intybus*), burnet (*Poterium polygamum*) and plantain (*Plantago lanceolata*) are highly mineral-efficient and their inclusion in a ley may, therefore, be desirable, provided they are not allowed to become dominant.

The type of weeds present will depend in the first place on the type of soil, whether heavy clay or light sand, whether chalk or peat, whether hungry or rich. Climate has also considerable influence on the flora, and rainfall and temperature are factors to be considered when forecasting what weeds are likely to appear. The moisture content of the soil must also be borne in mind and a high water table or periodic flooding will mean a preponderance of weed species which revel in such conditions.

In established grassland, weeds are frequently indicative of deficiencies of plant food in the soil. Sheep's sorrel (*Rumex acetosella*), for example, is an indication of soil acidity and the need for lime, while the presence of hard-head or knapweed (*Centaurea nigra*) in quantity is often coincident with phosphate deficiency. One must be careful, therefore, when trying to eliminate weeds in established grassland, to follow up with the necessary fertiliser treatment to encourage the desired grasses and clovers. In some cases it may be desirable to sow additional seed to fill in the bare ground left by the dead weeds. Modified seeds mixtures for this purpose are usually referred to as "renovation mixtures." In other words, weed eradication is merely part of the programme of grassland improvement.

Quite apart from the depressing effect weeds may have on the productivity of a sward by utilising space which should be occupied by what the farmers regard as the rightful tenants of the soil—the productive grasses and clovers—they may in some instances be harmful to livestock. One such weed is ragwort (*Senecio jacobaea*).

Ragwort is common on the poorer soils such as the Breckland heaths of Suffolk and elsewhere; it is classified as an injurious weed and county agricultural committees have powers to order occupiers of land to take suitable steps for its destruction. It was often associated with high rabbit populations, before myxomatosis effected natural control, for the grass was weakened by the very close grazing of the rabbits and the surface was broken by scratching, giving ideal conditions for weed invasion. Since rabbits avoid ragwort, a plant which seeds profusely, it was not long before the plant became a major menace. The plant is poisonous in all stages of growth and whether fresh or dry. Horses and cattle are most susceptible to it and although sheep may eat small quantities without ill-effect large quantities are harmful to them. Moreover, the plant thrives in severe droughts and under such conditions may be the only herbage available to the grazing stock with consequent increase in risk. It is in hay, however, that ragwort is most dangerous. Stock cannot easily discriminate between ragwort and the other dried plants making up the hay and since the poison is cumulative, small amounts taken over a long period may prove fatal. The symptoms of poisoning may be long in appearing and it may be anything from two weeks to three months before a "tucked-in" appearance, loss of condition, constipation and a constant straining to pass fæces indicates that something is wrong with the animal. Death may then follow within a few days.

Good grassland husbandry is often the answer, for ragwort will not invade a grass field in a state of good fertility. When grasses and clovers are encouraged into vigorous growth by sound fertilising it will gradually retreat, even if well established, as the productive species become more and more aggressive.

Buttercups may also prove poisonous to cattle. The three commonest grassland species, creeping buttercup (*Ranunculus repens*), meadow buttercup (*R. acris*) and bulbous buttercup (*R. bulbosus*) all contain an acrid poison. The first may be eaten by cattle in moderation with no ill-effects but both meadow buttercup and bulbous buttercup, when eaten fresh, have proved fatal. Fortunately, however, stock leave the buttercups ungrazed because of the bitter taste, unless very short of food. Buttercups become innocuous when dried in hay.

Another weed which sometimes causes trouble is the wild onion (*Allium vineale*), which occurs on sandy and clay soils. When eaten by dairy cattle the plant imparts a flavour of garlic to the milk. Provided, however, the plant is mown before the bulbils mature in the inflorescences, food reserves become exhausted and the spread is checked. In severe cases of infestation by far the best procedure is to plough out and thoroughly clean the land by fallowing before re-seeding again. Alternatively, the field in question can be put through an arable rotation.

Yarrow (*Achillea millefolium*) is highly mineral efficient and is included in some seed mixtures. In some pastures it may become so dominant that it will be eaten too freely. It will then impart a bitter and somewhat aromatic flavour to both milk and butter, due to the presence of an alkaloid. This is likely to happen, however, only on old neglected pastures.

Other troublesome weeds are the parasites yellow rattle (*Rhinanthus minor*) and broomrape (*Orobanche minor*). Yellow rattle is a partial parasite and attaches itself by means of suckers on its roots to the roots of grasses, thus robbing them of essential nutrients. Broomrape is wholly parasitic on clover and has no green leaves, simply a fleshy stem with brown scales. A large specimen may kill a clover plant when it becomes attached to the roots.

Until comparatively recent times the control of weeds in pastures was attempted mainly by mechanical means. Regular mowing to prevent the weeds from seeding, first by hand and later by machine, or harrowing, which usually effects more severe mechanical damage on the weeds than on the grasses present, can be quite effective. Good drainage is absolutely essential if the more productive species are to be encouraged, for without it rushes and other water-loving weeds will thrive. Moreover, the soil soon becomes sour when waterlogged and the herbage deteriorates. The full utilisation of hill grazing depends on good drainage and, where the cost of tile drainage is prohibitive or not likely to yield economic returns, open drains may be cut with mechanical power. These simple drains last from ten to fifteen years where only sheep graze the hills, but their effective life is reduced to no more than four to six years should cattle be introduced.

A growing menace on a large acreage of hill and moorland is bracken (*Pteridium aquilinum*), the control of which illustrates how machines and animals can be used effectively. The menace of bracken lies in the dense canopy of foliage produced, with the result that grasses and clovers are unable to survive the very effective shading. Thus productivity of the land falls rapidly unless control measures are instituted. The plant was once cut regularly to supply bedding for animals, since cereal crops were considered unsuitable on high ground and so there was no straw for bedding. Regular cutting—usually by hand scythe and later with a mowing machine—was generally carried out too late for effective control since the critical stage in the life of the plant is just before the final unfolding of the leaves. At this time the rhizomes are fully exhausted of the food supplies stored up and the leaves have not reached a point where photosynthesis is adequate to allow food reserves to be passed back into the root system. Efficient machines are now available for bruising or slashing bracken and these have been found to be most effective in controlling the plant. Bracken-covered land is frequently of difficult contour and often boulder-strewn and machines must have few moving parts and be simple in action but of strong construction to stand up to such heavy and difficult work.

In very severe cases of bracken infestation it may be desirable to cut the fern twice a year for a few years, with an interval of about five to six weeks between the cuttings. This has such a weakening effect on the plants that they ultimately succumb, especially if grasses and clovers are encouraged to develop at the same time.

Under certain conditions, treading by stock can be as effective as bruising by machine and in New Zealand flocks of sheep are repeatedly driven over land which is infested by bracken just when the fronds are in the "hook" stage of unfoldment. Evidence of the effectiveness of this treatment can be seen on any bracken moor in this country where it will be noticed that the paths trodden regularly by cattle, sheep, and horses are free of bracken, which may be growing vigorously each side of the track.

Animals also exert considerable influence in the control of weeds in pastures, not merely by the mechanical hoof damage noted above in the case of bracken, but by the action of grazing. Heavy stocking results in close grazing, which tends to keep many weeds in check automatically, and when the heavy stocking is associated with wise manuring to promote the development of the best species of herbage plants, the more pernicious weeds are unlikely to gain entry to the sward. Alternatively, if they are already established they are likely to be gradually ousted by the vigorously growing superior species. Many a field of worthless bent has been converted to a respectable pasture containing perennial ryegrass and white clover by the simple expedient of giving a generous application of basic slag in the autumn, followed by stocking heavily throughout the grazing season. However, the influence of the grazing animal may act in the reverse direction, for indiscriminate grazing can convert a ryegrass sward to bent. Careful timing of the grazing and skilful adjusting of the numbers of stock to the growth of grass at a particular time are essential.

Procumbent weeds common on arable land, such as knotgrass (*Polygonum aviculare*), can be a very serious problem when sowing down. Not readily controlled by mowing, long before the seedling grasses are sufficiently well established to permit grazing an adverse smothering influence on the sown species may be exerted. Seedling docks (*Rumex* spp.) and creeping thistles (*Cirsium arvense*), for example, are easily controlled in a young ley, but the mature plants in a well established pasture present a very different problem.

The use of chemicals for weed control in grassland has grown rapidly since 1945, when a new range of chemical substances was introduced to farming. Broad-leaved weeds in grassland, like the buttercup, dock and thistle, which always presented the farmer with many practical problems when control measures were contemplated, can now be controlled effectively by new selective herbicides. The majority of these possess chemical names and structural formulæ which are too long and cumbersome for frequent use and so most have been given either a coined name approved by the British Standards Institution or an abbreviation. Those used on grassland include MCPA, 2,4D, MCPB, 2,4DB, and dinoseb. Care is necessary to ensure the correct dilution and rate of application, and to choose the most effective time to spray. Moreover, precautions must be taken to prevent the spray drifting on to susceptible crops, especially if those crops belong to a neighbour!

Unwanted grasses are often the chief offenders in established grassland and until the recent introduction of dalapon (2,2 dichloro-proprionic acid), a translocated herbicide toxic primarily to grasses, there appeared to be little chance of controlling them by chemical means. Dalapon has already been used extensively for the destruction of unwanted grasses in arable land, and it may be found possible to use it for selective killing of agriculturally undesirable constituents of a sward. A good deal of experimental work is necessary before this chemical can be prescribed for general use.

The advent of the group of chemicals known as the bipyridyliums, which include Diquat and Paraquat, has set in motion the development of completely new techniques for grassland improvement and arable cropping. These herbicides act on the green parts of plants, killing the aerial shoots quite quickly. They possess the added advantage of being rainfast, so that if rain should fall soon after spraying the effect is not diminished. In addition, when the chemical comes into contact with the soil it is immediately inactivated. In chemical language it is said to be adsorbed (i.e. locked) on to the clay particles and thus there is no residual activity which is the drawback to many herbicides like, say, sodium chlorate, which may sterilise the soil for as long as five months. Thus, when Paraquat is used, as soon as the herbage has been killed fertilisers and seeds can be drilled into the dead vegetation and the process of renovation commences without delay. Other crops like the cereals and kale and rape have been successfully grown in this way— an operation known as "sod seeding" because the seeds are implanted into the unploughed sod or soil—and the method is generally described as "ploughless farming."

It is particularly adapted for land of difficult contour where more orthodox methods of cultivation are dangerous or impossible, and it certainly offers a solution to the problem of renewing under-productive permanent pasture in such circumstances. The chemicals can be used also for clearing weedy stubbles after harvest and prior to ploughing, or indeed, for killing a turf prior to drilling a forage crop like kale. On the sticky clay soils the problem of poaching seriously restricts the facility with which kale can be grazed by dairy cows or sheep. If, however, the kale seed is drilled into the treated turf which is not ploughed, the grazing animals have much firmer conditions and grazing is greatly facilitated. I have often seen cows in winter time when grazing kale grown by normal methods up to their bellies in mud and slush. So, for these conditions, "ploughless farming," using the new herbicides, will prove an immense boon to cattle and farmer.

In addition to the broad-leaved weeds already discussed, in moorland areas and on rough grazings a number of herbaceous weeds such as bracken (discussed above) and rushes, with the woody weeds such as bramble, gorse, heather, and bilberry, complicate the issue. Chemicals are available to control these but they are so drastic in action that of necessity the sowing of seed as a follow-up measure with appropriate dressings of fertilisers is essential.

The presence of weeds in a pasture is regarded generally by most farmers as an indication of lack of efficiency in managing their land and crops. A weedy pasture is rightly considered a sign of slovenly farming, although it must be admitted right away that the same degree of scorn is not poured upon such farmers as upon those having weedy arable land. We have still a long way to go, alas, before grass is treated as a crop in its own right and given the same respect bestowed without question upon cereals or root crops.

Apart from the obvious cases, however, where weeds are poisonous to livestock or cause taints in the milk and must be eliminated as soon as possible, is there a clear case for the control of weeds in grassland? What is the effect of weeds on grassland productivity? There are some obvious examples. The spear thistle (*Cirsium vulgare*) forms a rosette of leaves at ground level often reaching at least two feet in diameter. As the leaves end in stiff, yellowish spines, grazing stock not unnaturally dislike them, since their noses, lips and tongues are pricked to the point of causing discomfort. The result is that the grasses mingling with the thistle will be untouched and waste follows. In one case of severe infestation no less than ten per cent of the grazing area was left untouched by the animals on this account alone. The creeping thistle, although a smaller plant, is equally disliked by stock, and since it spreads rapidly, soon covers and renders useless a considerable acreage of grass. The elimination of thistles, therefore, is obviously desirable. Unfortunately, however, this aspect of weed control has received less attention from research workers.

Halliday and Templeman, on treating leys and permanent pasture with M.C.P.A., found a significant increase in the yield of useful grasses and legumes in a sward. It is interesting to note also that when the herbicide was applied in addition to a nitrogenous fertiliser the increased yield was very much greater, indicating that the grasses were better able to utilise applied nitrogen when they were not in competition with weeds. The evidence which is available at the moment, therefore, indicates that chemicals in many instances can eradicate weeds more quickly than normal methods of cultivation, although not necessarily at the same or lower costs, which is the crucial test applied by the farmer. None the less, herbicides are an important additional tool towards ensuring good grassland management.

CHAPTER 9

PESTS AND DISEASES OF GRASSLAND

Farmers and gardeners are well aware of the many diseases and insect pests which attack their crops and demand timely and effective control measures if the well-being of the crops is to be safe-guarded and the harvest assured. Yet how many realise that grass itself may be subject to attack by pest and disease and unless the problem is tackled with the thoroughness given without question to crops like potatoes, sugar beet or cereals, the yield of herbage must inevitably be reduced? Only in recent years, since the recognition of grass as a crop and the increasing exploitation of its immense potential, have many of the insect pests and diseases affecting the growth of the grass plant received sufficient attention from research workers. More-over, the new conception of what constitutes the ideal sward has inevitably focused attention on this problem. When the sward was composed, by design and self-intrusion, of many species of grasses, clovers, and miscellaneous plants, it was of little moment if one species succumbed to insect pest or disease. Under such circumstances there was an adequacy of other species to take its place and the change in the composition of the sward would in all likelihood pass quite unnoticed. This cannot be the case when a field is sown with a single strain of a single species or at most two or three strains in conjunction with white or red clover. Under such conditions the loss of a strain can be a very serious matter for the farmer. Since grass seed production in this country has developed into an industry, the problem of con-trolling insect pests and disease has become even more important.

Insect pests attack the grass plant at three points: the roots, the leaves and stems, and the flower-heads and seed heads. First, the roots. These may be attacked by such pests as wireworms, leatherjackets or the larvæ of the chafer beetle which eat into and sever the roots. When the attack is sufficiently concentrated to damage a large number of roots the plant may succumb. Even if it is only partially damaged, the growth of the grass must inevitably be adversely affected. Of the insects which live in grassland over sixty-five per cent are to be found in the top inch and a half of the soil, whereas in arable land only twenty-five per cent are found in this region, the remainder inhabiting the deeper layers.

Wireworms (*Agriotes* spp.) are the larvæ of several species of click beetle and are amongst the most serious pests. When grassland is ploughed up for arable cropping the young growing seedlings of cereal or sugar beet are attacked just below ground level, the wire-worms eating into the roots. This damage is soon noticed, for the young seedlings die and leave gaps in the crop. In grassland also, wireworms are constantly attacking the grass roots. In established grass there is little damage to be seen, but evidence is accumulating that recently-sown leys may be injured to such an extent that it may be necessary to patch the ley with new seed, or even to re-seed entirely. The normal control measure for a wireworm population of less than 600,000 per acre is to apply an insecticidal seed dressing, but if heavier infestations are noted then it is more usual to work the insecticide into the seed bed or compound it with the fertiliser for use in a combined seed and fertiliser drill. It is possible to speak in such astronomical numbers of a pest in the soil because in practice it is relatively easy to determine the total population per acre by taking a sample of soil with an augur, and counting the wireworms by eye. They can also be floated out on brine. This is a service carried out for farmers by members of the National Agricultural Advisory Service. During the war years of 1939-45, when a large acreage of old per-manent grass was ploughed up for arable cropping, this precaution saved countless thousands of acres growing cereals and beet which might otherwise have been lost. I frequently came across cases where the wireworm count was over a million per acre, and without this knowledge, which enables the essential control measures to be adopted, the crop would have been a total failure.

Attacks by leatherjackets, which are the larvæ of the crane fly or daddy longlegs (*Tipula paludosa*), can also be serious. The fly lays its eggs in grass or clover fields in late summer, and the brown legless grubs, which attain a length of about an inch, eat their way through the plants at, or slightly below, ground level. Unlike the damage caused by wireworms, there is seldom any wilting or discoloration of the plant to indicate that something is amiss. While wireworms live in the soil for several years, the leatherjackets have a life of only nine months before changing into a pupa. Thus an arable field is not infested for more than one season. Severe damage on established grassland is not common, but lawns, bowling greens and golf courses, where short herbage is maintained, may suffer badly. From time to time large acreages of re-seeded grassland have been severely damaged, as in Yorkshire in 1944-5 and in many other parts of the country in 1951-2. In many of these cases the attacks were of sufficient severity to cause complete failure and acres were eaten bare of all herbage. The usual treatment for leatherjackets is to broadcast over the field a poisoned bait, consisting of moistened bran mixed with D.D.T. or B.H.C.

Chafer beetle larvæ cause sporadic damage, but this can be serious at times, and the grass roots over large areas can be severed in such numbers as to leave dead turf lying like pieces of coconut matting on the surface. The attack may commence in summer and continue until early winter, and frequently only the strongly-rooted plants like dandelion, yarrow, and cocksfoot manage to survive. Trials have indicated that some degree of control may be obtained following an application of B.H.C. dust to infested grassland. In many cases, unfortunately, it means ploughing out and starting afresh, or sowing a renovation mixture of grasses or clovers. The cockchafer (*Melolontha melolontha*) and the garden chafer (*Phyllopertha horticola*) are usually the most troublesome, although on occasion the green rosechafer (*Cetonia aurata*) has been known to do serious damage.

Secondly the vegetative part of the plant may be attacked, the pest eating the leaves and stems of the plant, or perhaps boring into the tissues and feeding there, but whichever line of attack is adopted the yield of herbage and of seed is seriously reduced.

In hill districts the caterpillars of the antler moth (*Cerapteryx graminis*) attack bent, Molinia, fescues, and Nardus, although, for some reason not yet explained, it seems that meadow foxtail and wild red clover are often left alone. In 1927, an outbreak was recorded at over 2,000 feet on the Plynlimmon range and in this instance seagulls came to the rescue and consumed the caterpillars which were doing the damage. An attack may start in a small isolated area but the invading army grows in numbers very rapidly and usually moves in one direction across an area so that it is possible to cut off the attack by digging a trench across the line of approach and spraying the trench at intervals with a suitable insecticide. A full-scale attack is an awe-inspiring sight. In some cases it may be advisable to burn the affected areas, using flame guns; in others, a poison bait of bran and Paris green has proved successful. In the southern Pennines the larvæ have sometimes been found to be parasitised, and this, with the willing help of the seagulls, has proved adequate for controlling the pest.

In the Midlands, the yellow mound ant (*Lasius flavus*) may reduce the yield and edibility of the herbage on large acreages of grassland. The ants do not feed on the herbage, but their tunnelling activities, and the hills of soil so formed, cut off essential water supplies from the grass roots. Moreover, several species of aphids may live in an ant hill, and, unlike the ants, actually feed on the grass roots. Affected grassland needs to be drastically harrowed using spiked implements which will tear out the ant hills and spread the soil. This treatment must be followed up by a suitable application of fertilisers to feed the grass and encourage the remaining plants to fill up and knit together to form a turf again. In very severe cases re-seeding may be necessary.

It is not uncommon for the grass aphids (*Metopolophium festucæ* and *Rhopalosiphum padi*), to cause damage to grassland by attacking the tips of the leaves, which usually turn red, the remainder of the plant turning yellow. As the cell-sap is depleted the plants turn brown and finally die. Severe damage usually necessitates renovation or re-seeding.

In humid seasons such as 1959, slugs and snails may occur in such large numbers that a pasture can be denuded of leafage. Usually the clovers suffer more than the grasses and in one recorded case it was estimated that the loss in yield per acre of green herbage was nine tons. Fortunately in such cases very effective control is obtained by broadcasting at dusk—when the marauders come out to feed—a mixture of copper sulphate (18 lb. per acre) and Kainit (3 cwt. per acre).

Thirdly, insect pests may attack the flower-heads and seed heads of the grasses which, should seed production be the reason for growing the crop, can result in serious financial loss to the farmer. The gall midges (*Cecidomyidæ*) are amongst the most important pests in this class. The eggs are laid in the flower-heads and the larvæ feed on the flowering parts or developing seed of cocksfoot, meadow foxtail, or timothy. It is important when contemplating seed production to avoid low-lying, heavily sheltered fields likely to harbour the midges and to select in preference high-lying, exposed fields so far as possible. Moreover, it is always a wise precaution to run the drill rows in the same direction as the prevailing winds, for this helps to prevent the midges from settling.

When cocksfoot is grown for seed the caterpillars of the cocksfoot moth (*Glyphipteryx cramerella*) may cause serious damage, especially in the case of indigenous strains. Burning the stubble after the combine harvester has dealt with the crop substantially reduces infestation the following year.

The diseases of grass are just as numerous as the insect pests and again frequently go unnoticed or occasion little concern because, in the main, they are of minor economic importance. In any event, control measures would not be economically worth while except in special circumstances. Many of the cereal diseases also affect the grasses but in the case of the cereals, grown for one specific purpose, the problem of control is regarded quite differently and considered a matter for general cultural routine.

In recent years even non-agriculturists have noted rust on grasses; indeed who would not, when one's shoes, after strolling across affected grassland, are covered in a bright orange powder! Crown rust (*Puccinia coronata*) is common on a number of our grasses, especially perennial ryegrass, and is responsible for some loss of leaf, although the most serious effect is to make the grass unpalatable. At this stage the whole field looks yellow and the trouble is most noticeable in the autumn, particularly in Wales and the south and east of England. The alternative host is buckthorn (*Rhamnus cathartica*), whilst older buckthorn (*Frangula alnus*) is an alternative host for some races of the crown rust fungus. The spores survive the winter so that the infection carries on from season to season. It is not uncommon for timothy to fail in establishment on account of stem rust (*Puccinia graminis* var. *phlei-pratensis*), for this grass is not an aggressive one like cocksfoot. Resistant strains for both hay and pasture have been bred at Aberystwyth. Cocksfoot is most susceptible to yellow rust (*Puccinia glumarum*), and seed crops can be seriously affected.

The economic importance of mildew (*Erysiphe graminis*) on grasses is much more difficult to assess than in the case of the cereals. The "mildewed" appearance of the plants, especially during dry summers, is quite easily noticed and as the disease gains hold, the plants turn a sickly yellow and are evidently not thriving. They are seldom killed outright and although the palatability of the herbage is impaired, there is no other obvious effect of the disease.

Choke (*Epichloe typhina*) occurs on several grasses, particularly cocksfoot and timothy, reducing the yield of seed by 25 to 30 per cent. The disease is so named because of the white felt of fungus developing out of the leaves and surrounding the young flower stalk, which often fails to develop as a result. The trouble is not usually noticed until May, and the felt changes from white to yellow, and then to orange, as the summer advances. Being perennial, the fungus is carried over in the stems and leaves, but can also be carried in the seed. In severe cases of infection the only sensible means of control in the case of seed crops is to plough up.

The ryegrasses are sometimes affected by blind seed disease (*Gloeotinia temulenta*), and if the fungus infects the flowers the development of the seed may be prevented or its germination impaired; hence the disease's name. Seed infected later in the season may still germinate and this serves to carry the disease over to another season, but the fungus does not live long in the dry seed and, if this is stored for two years, it may then be used with safety. For new seed, which has been infected, disinfection by immersion for twenty minutes in a 0·25 per cent solution of an organo-mercurial fungicide at 50° C. has proved effective.

Many readers will doubtless have seen in the seed heads of grasses, sometimes on rye and the ryegrasses, small black bodies, about $\frac{1}{3}$ in. to $\frac{3}{4}$ in. long, which replace some of the grains in the ear. These are ergots (*Claviceps purpurea*), which have been recognised for many years as a cause of poisoning to humans and livestock alike. Cases have been recorded of horses dying two to three days after eating ergotised hay or rye, while in 1927-8, cases of ergotism occurred in Manchester among humans who had eaten affected ryebread. This was traced to rye crops which had suffered severely from the fungus in 1927.

When mature, the ergots fall to the ground or are mixed with the seed at harvest time and, germinating the following spring, infect the flowers of the host plant by means of spores. The trouble is most common in cool, damp weather, and insects help to carry the spores from plant to plant. It is also claimed that ergots may cause abortion in cows and sheep but this is very difficult to prove, due to the incidence of contagious abortion in farm livestock caused by *Brucella abortus*.

In all probability we shall see less and less of this trouble in the future because of the insistence now placed on cutting hay crops at the early flowering stage in an effort to secure a higher quality product. This is fortunate, for no specific control measures are practicable. Clean farming as a means of eliminating weeds which may act as host plants and the trimming of hedges and banks are the most profitable lines of attack. The last season when ergots were noticeably present was 1965, which was exceptionally wet and favourable for the fungus.

Of small consequence to the grass crop, but important elsewhere, is take-all (*Ophiobolus graminis*), which is frequently seen on the roots of ryegrasses, cocksfoot and timothy, as well as of the weed grasses. The disease can do serious damage to the wheat crop, and diseased grass roots are often the means of carrying on the infection for a longer period than would be the case if the soil was cultivated. The fungus invades seedlings from the soil through the rooting system, and affected rootlets appear black or threaded with black when carefully examined after washing. As the disease spreads, the lower part of the stem may be affected and plants may die. If they eventually succeed in forming ears, the ears are white and develop very little grain. Hence "white-heads," the name by which the disease is commonly known. There are no varieties of cereal which are resistant to the disease and the only possible control measure is to adopt an appropriate crop rotation. Weed grasses such as couch, bent and Yorkshire fog may serve as carriers of infection. If the soil can be kept free from such harbouring agencies for more than a year the fungus will tend to disappear and it then becomes safe to sow a wheat crop again. It is interesting to note in passing that while barley is equally susceptible to take-all the disease seems to stay in the roots without doing any appreciable damage to the crop.

Most people who habitually walk over grassland which is kept closely mown or grazed are familiar with fairy rings. The ever widening ring of dark green herbage is attributed to the stimulation of the grass by the additional nitrogen made available by the action of the fungus on organic matter in the soil. Behind the fairy ring is left an inner circle of dead or dying grass, the reason for which is obscure. One theory is that this area becomes akin to a mat and absorbs rain and dew so very slowly that conditions of virtual drought exist in the area and the herbage dies for want of water. In the dry summers of 1936 and 1947, fairy rings and their effect on pasture production were particularly noticeable in many parts of the country.

CHAPTER 10

THE INFLUENCE OF THE ANIMAL

Every grazing animal has its own characteristic method of securing herbage. Horses, for instance, part the lips and nip the grass off between the upper and lower incisor teeth. This means they are able to graze close to the ground and so a short, dense sward suits them best. Since the horse is a non-ruminant it must masticate its food while still in the act of grazing, much as we eat our food, and so horses are much slower grazers than cattle or sheep which swallow grass as quickly as they obtain it, only to regurgitate it for thorough mastication—chewing the cud—later on.

The cow curls its tongue round the herbage, pulls it into the mouth and tears it off, using the incisors of the lower jaw and the dental pad of the upper to hold the herbage firm. Cows spend about eight hours of each day in grazing, a further seven hours in chewing the cud, and the remaining nine in resting, either standing or lying down, and in walking to and from the water trough or other source of water supply. The strange thing is that these times are more or less independent of the amount of herbage available. An average cow, weighing around 10 cwt., requires in the region of 150 lb. of grass daily to satisfy her appetite. If the grass be scanty, as in a poor field, or during a protracted drought, or in the very early spring before growth fully commences, or in autumn when growth is much slower, the cow cannot secure sufficient food during its eight-hour grazing period. The animal then literally starves, losing flesh and "milking off its back": in other words, using up body reserves to offset the paucity of its daily ration.

The grazing mechanism of sheep is different again. The thin lips are parted and the herbage is bitten off between the low incisor teeth which close tightly against the dental pad of the upper jaw. This is similar to the methods of cattle, but here the similarity ends, for sheep do not use the tongue as a prehensile organ to wrap around the herbage and draw it into the mouth. Thus sheep can graze very closely, indeed more closely than any other grass-eating animal, except the rabbit and the guinea pig. The ideal grass sward for sheep is, therefore, short and of maximum density. The close grazing habits of sheep mean, of course, that they will find a living where other farm animals would starve. At the same time, however, such intensive defoliation, if practised year after year, results in a serious lowering of the yield of grass annually produced by the sward, for the development of the finer-bladed grasses and legumes, especially wild white clover, then becomes excessive. Small wonder that cattle dislike to follow sheep in grazing a pasture for they are fully aware that the sheep have taken the best of the sward. On the other hand, many weeds distasteful to cattle often seem to be relished by sheep. Ragwort, for instance, which may cause poisoning in cattle, is grazed down readily by sheep, and exploitation of this lack of discrimination was in days gone by a means of controlling the weed.

There are other noticeable differences in the grazing behaviour of animals. Horses refuse to consume tainted herbage and if they are left in a pasture alone, they make their dung in one corner of the field and graze the rest. The odd corner soon becomes rough with uneaten herbage while the dung, which is a source of plant food, aggravates the whole problem by encouraging further growth. Thus much valuable grass is wasted, and the field soon becomes very unsightly. Sheep are by no means so discriminating in their grazing habits and while cattle will not consume herbage which is tainted with dung or urine they certainly are not so fastidious as to use only part of the field for dunging. While stock are reluctant to consume herbage tainted by their own kind they are not so concerned about the herbage tainted by other species. So if one grazes a field with sheep, horses and cattle, much more uniform grazing is obtained than if the field is grazed by one species only.

The aim of the grazier is to provide his stock with highly nutritious herbage, making sure that it is of the right length for the different classes of livestock; horses and sheep on the one hand and cattle on the other. In order to secure the best measure of utilisation and reduce waste to a minimum, tainting of the herbage must be limited. For this reason the old practice of soiling or cutting crops green and feeding them direct to the stock, now called "zero grazing" or mechanical grazing, has much to commend it. The herbage can be mown at its maximum feeding value, gathered up without waste, and fed in troughs to the stock. The danger of tainting due to dunging is thus completely eliminated. A compromise adopted by many farmers is to alternate grazing with mowing. The droppings and urine from the grazing assist the re-growth of grass and the second crop can then be mown for silage. By the time the third crop is ready, the tainting effect of the earlier grazing will be largely dissipated.

The effects of grazing on the grasses themselves are also important. Grasses store food in their root systems for use in winter time and these food reserves are utilised to produce early growth in spring. To provide an early bite, therefore, the grasses must have adequate reserves and this is ensured by appropriate rest periods during the previous autumn. If when a grass is making active growth, that growth is removed as fast as it is produced, the food reserves in the rooting system will soon be exhausted and the plant will be weakened. Should the practice be persistent over a number of years, the plant will ultimately die out. Perennial ryegrass, for instance, makes its maximum effort in spring between mid-March and mid-April, and heavy grazing at this time of year, therefore, exhausts the food reserves in the rooting system and weakens the plant. Should such heavy grazing be repeated for three or four years in succession the pasture will be denuded of perennial ryegrass. The critical period for cocks-foot is mid-April to mid-May and for timothy from mid-May to mid-June. If robust plants of these species are to be safe-guarded, then repeated grazing must be avoided so far as possible during these critical periods. The best grazing practice indicates that it is unwise to take an early bite from any particular field more frequently than one year in four. Heavy and continuous grazing throughout the year and over a period of years tends to deplete the resources of the better grasses and they will gradually succumb, while low-growing, stolon-iferous species, such as *Agrostis* spp. or wild white clover, will escape much of this punishment owing to their habit of growth and in con-sequence will soon dominate the pasture.

Many years ago the influence of the grazing animal on the com-position of the sward was demonstrated. It was shown that one could bring about a dominance of ryegrass, cocksfoot, timothy or white clover, or even of weeds, simply by varying the type and intensity of stocking and the general grazing practice during any particular year. It is now recognised that "on-and-off" grazing best secures a good balance between the useful grasses and clovers while ensuring that the productive species maintain their supremacy, and weeds are kept in suppression. This simply means that when the grass shows four to five inches of growth the stock are turned out and the concentration of stock is adjusted by numbers or age or type to consume that herbage in the minimum space of time. The field is then rested and allowed to make further growth. When four to five inches are again available, the cycle recommences. Most pastures will give four such grazings in the course of the year, each successive grazing being less efficient for the reasons already given. Some impressions of the influence of grazing management on the botanical composition of the sward can be gleaned from Fig. 3. The ideal stage of growth for grazing cannot be accurately assessed. The longer the rest period between grazings, the greater the amount of grass present but, alas, the lower the quality of the herbage. Until recently, rest periods of thirty to forty days were regarded as providing the ideal compromise between yield and quality of herbage, but as a result of detailed experiments, it has been suggested that the rest period must vary with the rapidity with which the grass grows. Thus the rest period in spring will be much shorter than in high summer or during a drought. The rest period in a wet season will be shorter than in a dry year like 1964. The grazing periods, however, must remain constant. When growth is poor, therefore, areas of grassland previously mown for hay or silage will be used for grazing, while in periods of rapid growth less acreage will be needed and the surplus pasture will be mown for conservation. Deterioration in the vigour and productivity of a sward is brought about by frequent grazings during poor growing conditions.

This means that a field to be mown for hay or silage should be grazed between cuttings, so that it is not mown for hay repeatedly, but only once in three or four years, for repeated mowing is even worse for the field than repeated grazing. Wherever practicable, mowing should be alternated with "on-and-off" grazing, the whole forming a rotational system of grazing attuned both to the needs of the stock and the needs of the pasture. The following is an outline of such a system:

1st year: Grass allowed to make good growth before grazing commences in spring. After hard grazing a rest period is allowed and this sequence is followed throughout the season until early autumn when the field is given a good rest to allow food stores to be built up in the rooting system. With the aid of an early application of nitrogenous fertiliser the following February this ensures:

2nd year: Early "bite" in April to May after which the field can be shut up and subsequent growth mown for silage.

3rd year: Hard and continuous grazing throughout the year

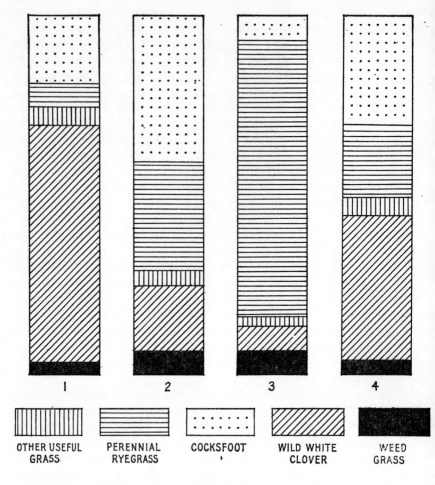

FIG. 3. THE INFLUENCE OF GRAZING ON BOTANICAL COMPOSITION
OF THE SWARD

1 Grazed continuously
2 Rested mid-March until mid-April
3 Rested mid-April to mid-May: grazed rest of year
4 Grazed "on and off" from early spring until early autumn

encourages the finer grasses and clovers and keeps the coarser grasses in check.

4th year: The balance between the grasses and clovers is adjusted by taking an early cut for hay. This keeps the clovers in check and the early grasses are allowed to make good growth which strengthens them.

The aftermath is lightly grazed by mixed stock and the field is closed in September ready to commence the 4-year sequence once more.

Clearly there is far more to managing a pasture than merely opening the gate in the early days of the spring, turning stock in, and finally closing the gate in the late autumn which is the common impression of the simple life of the grassland farmer. To illustrate this point here is an analysis of two fields, one grazed indiscriminately, i.e. over-grazed in spring, when the grass is scarce, and under-grazed in summer when the amount of grass is beyond the capacity of the stock to consume it, the other grazed on the rotational sequence just outlined above:

TABLE 7.   COMPOSITION OF THE SWARD

	Indiscriminate Grazing				Rotational Grazing			
Composition of the Sward	1st yr.	2nd yr.	3rd yr.	4th yr.	1st yr.	2nd yr.	3rd yr.	4th yr.
Good grasses	65	54	40	27	65	63	59	60
White clover	33	40	48	51	33	34	37	36
Weeds	2	6	12	22	2	3	4	4
	100	100	100	100	100	100	100	100

Clearly, by rotational grazing the composition of the sward has remained fairly constant. By way of contrast, the indiscriminate grazing by stock has brought about a serious deterioration, as shown by the weed population at the end of four years.

Adequate fencing and watering are also important factors in grazing management. The fences must be kept in good order to prevent stock from wandering from one field to another, especially since straying stock may cause serious damage to arable crops. An adequate supply of clean water is essential and water troughs should be available in every pasture field. The expense of installing such troughs can be limited by using alkathene tubing and movable galvanised troughs.

During the 1914-18 war, Germany was short of concentrated animal feeding stuffs. An adequate supply of synthetic nitrogenous fertilisers ensured the maximum production from grassland, and proper management of this went far towards offsetting the lack of concentrated foods. The Hohenheim system of grassland management was the system the Germans adopted. This consisted of supplying to the dairy cow throughout the grazing season young grass about four inches long. This diet, given to appetite, ensures adequate nutrition for both the maintenance of the animal and the production of four to five gallons of milk without any other food being given. The grassland received lime, phosphate and potash as a basal fertiliser dressing and the area was divided by simple wire fencing into a number of paddocks, each permitting a grazing density of ten cows to an acre. Thus to graze a herd of fifty cows, each paddock must measure five acres. Six paddocks were required in all, with a water supply laid on to each. Sulphate of ammonia was applied to the first paddock about the end of February or March to encourage early grass production and to the others in sequence at intervals of about ten days. By so doing, a continuity of growth was obtained and when the herbage of the first paddock was consumed, the second paddock was at the ideal stage of growth for cattle to enter; thence to the third paddock, and so on until they had grazed all six. Immediately the cattle left, each paddock was harrowed to spread the droppings, received another application of nitrogenous fertiliser, and was then shut up. The first paddock was ready for grazing, and in ideal condition, by the time the sixth paddock had been grazed down. The cows rotated round the six paddocks throughout the grazing season, and each paddock received about three or four applications of nitrogenous fertiliser.

To-day, the system is not practised in its original conception, but the lessons of those days, namely, the importance of concentrating stock on a small area of ground to utilise the grass at its maximum feeding value, and the advantage of always presenting milking cows with herbage of the right quality and leaving dry stock, sheep or other cattle, to consume the remains are still put into practice.

There were certain inherent snags in the system which have since been eradicated. To begin with, there was the problem of supplying the costly fencing. Then it was not always easy to supply water to each paddock. Above all, too much herbage might be produced in a season of good growth, so that by the time, say, the fourth paddock was grazed, the first was ready again, while in a dry season the reverse was true and when the cows had grazed the sixth paddock the first might not be ready for grazing the second time. In the first case, the remedy was to mow the fifth and sixth paddocks and make the herbage made into silage. To solve the problem of the second, an insurance crop had to be provided near at hand, or more than six paddocks had to be prepared.

The introduction of the electric fence altered the whole concept of the paddock system. The advantages of the Hohenheim system can now be obtained at a tenth of the cost. What is more, the electric fence is very much more flexible as a means of controlling grazing. It is one of the simplest, most ingenious devices introduced to farming in recent years and has undoubtedly revolutionised the control of livestock on grassland.

It consists of smooth wire, usually 14 s.w.g. because this size is thin enough to wind on a reel for easy transport from field to field and for rapid assembly and dismantling. It is supported on iron rods which have an insulated loop to carry the electrified wire and are pointed at the base, so that to erect them is a simple matter of pushing them into the ground every twenty yards or so, depending on circumstances. The wire can be adjusted for height to suit varying sizes of stock.

Most electric fences in this country are of the inductive discharge type and an induction coil steps up the voltage supplied by a 6-volt battery. A controller regulates the rate at which electric contact points open and close to give about fifty impulses a minute. As a result of the intermittent current little demand is made on the battery or accumulator, which lasts, therefore, about three weeks.

In concentrating the grazing on a small area of ground to ensure that the stock act with the same efficiency in removing the herbage as a mowing machine, it is necessary to have what is termed a back fence. Many farmers erect this within four yards of the first fence so that the stock are really feeding in a narrow corridor. The width of the corridor obviously varies with the size of the field and the number of stock grazing at any one time. One highly efficient grazier allows 110 cows on a corridor an acre and three quarters in area. They remain there for one day and then move on to the next corridor. As the highest milkers move forward daily, taking the finest herbage, the remnants are cleaned up by the low-yielding cows in the herd—those that are dry or getting towards the end of their lactation. Some farmers even move the electric fence twice a day, so important do they consider it that the high-yielding cows should have the finest quality food, closely regulated in amount to avoid wasting even a single blade of grass.

Simple though the electric fence may be in principle and practice, it demands the time of the cowman to erect and dismantle and some farmers are now dividing their grass fields into suitably sized small paddocks with permanent fencing—the electrified wires being fixed to permanent posts. Thus the stock rotate in exactly the same way as with a movable fence but the fields are already in being—of appropriate size according to the number of grazing cows—and the herd moves from one to the next simply by opening a gate.

Comparable grazing techniques are being used for sheep. Thus the concentration of large numbers of sheep on a relatively small area and ensuring that the lambs graze ahead of their mothers, thereby securing clean herbage free from disease, go hand in hand with fertiliser treatment and intensive methods of grass production. Further reference to this is made in chapter 14.

It is not uncommon for pigs, both sows and stores, to run out on grass, though in the later stages of fattening more concentrated foods and restricted exercise in sties and pens are necessary. Frequently small well-fenced enclosures are used and this intensive grazing results in over-manuring; the coarser grasses then predominate and become tufted, and the area becomes extremely unsightly. This is aggravated by the rooting of the pigs, which, if they are not ringed in the nose, damage the sward a good deal. The plan is only practicable, therefore, when the land is destined for early ploughing. The advantage of outdoor grazing lies in the pigs securing some of their food from the grass, and the consumption of meal is reduced by some 20 per cent with consequent economies in cost of foods. The pigs are healthier, although some provision is necessary for shade and shelter from sun, wind and rain. Regular liming and phosphating must be carried out.

Poultry, too, in the past were often kept in movable pens on grassland. This permits some reduction in the cost of foods particularly in the case of geese, which can obtain the bulk of their nutritional requirements from grass, while the droppings enrich the land for further crops.

CHAPTER II

THE INFLUENCE OF MAN

The extreme variety of our grass fields is one of the features which most overseas visitors notice almost on arrival. Not only is there considerable variation from field to field, but also from season to season, and, indeed, even in the course of one season. Some of the variation is due to the influence of the grazing animal *per se* and some to the skill of the farmer in manipulating his animals to make the best use of the grassland at his disposal. There are, however, many other influences at work.

Grass is a crop, and field experiments carried out in the nineteenth century showed that it required adequate supplies of nitrogen, phosphate, potash and lime if it was cut frequently. Under grazing conditions some of the plant nutrients are returned to the soil in the droppings and urine of the animals and so the grassland needs less fertiliser. When herbage is cut and removed, however, considerable amounts of plant nutrients are taken off the ground and the soil is accordingly impoverished. Clover needs both phosphate and potash to promote growth, and nitrogen for leaf production, i.e. increased yield of herbage.

In the last twenty years our knowledge of the effects of fertilisers on grass has greatly improved, but the application of this knowledge lags far behind the progress made with arable crops. There are several reasons to account for this unsatisfactory state of affairs. Grass must first be processed into meat or milk before it becomes saleable—apart from the sale of hay or dried grass which is of comparatively little moment—and a farmer, therefore, cannot draw up a balance sheet of profit and loss with the same ease as in the case of potatoes or wheat or any arable sales crop. Then, as we have seen, clovers play a considerable role in the feeding of the grasses with which they are associated and this masks the effect of nitrogenous fertilisers; there are still farmers who rely on leguminous plants to the exclusion of artificial fertilisers. Moreover, a good deal of our grassland is in the form of leys, which may be fertilised indirectly through other crops in the rotation. Indeed, all advice to-day suggests that one should fertilise for the whole rotation as a balanced unit rather than fertilise the crops as individuals. Nitrogenous fertilisers are then used as an additional tool to produce more grass when required.

Not until quite recently has it been possible to advise on the uses of nitrogenous fertilisers quantitatively for leys, or for pure grass swards cut for hay, silage or dried grass, or used for early bite. There is still no satisfactory scientific basis for the use of fertilisers on leys grazed in summer when optimum conditions for growth exist, nor is it possible from experimental evidence to offer general advice on the use of phosphates and potash. The Park Grass Plots at Rothamsted were laid down in 1856, and have yielded most useful evidence indicating how nitrogenous manuring must be balanced with adequate supplies of phosphate and potash if production is to be sustained, and how necessary potassium is to the growth of clovers. Later, the work at Cockle Park Experimental Station demonstrated the value of basic slag—a by-product of the steel industry—as a source of both lime and phosphate, with a particularly good influence on the growth of clovers. Subsequently the value was established of ground mineral phosphates as a source of phosphoric acid, particularly in the case of a heavy type of soil, preferably with a lime deficiency, in a district of high rainfall.

During the second world war, most of the phosphates and potash fertilisers had to be used on arable land for crops producing direct human food like potatoes, sugar beet, wheat and vegetables, and little experimental work could be carried out. Since 1946, however, a mass of experimental work has accumulated and it is now possible to advise on the manuring of grassland under a wide range of conditions.

The results of all this work indicate a linear relationship between the nitrogenous fertiliser applied and the response from the grass at all levels of manuring, 0·25 cwt/acre of nitrogen producing about 5 to 6 cwt. of additional hay. The data is insufficient to provide comparable figures for the effect of nitrogen on grazing land. So far as phosphate and potash are concerned, the average increase in yield of hay from 0·5 cwt. phosphoric acid and 0·5 cwt. potash per acre was about $2\frac{1}{2}$ to 3 cwt. per acre. Little information exists concerning swards cut for silage or drying, or used for grazing, and a farmer's experience of his land and its response to fertilisers still largely determines the fertiliser applications. The use of straight fertilisers is becoming less common and many farmers now use compounds, the basis of which in most cases is mono-ammonium phosphate.

The use of nitrogenous fertilisers early in the year produces extra grass before normal growth commences, which is usually referred to as "early bite," while an application in late summer extends seasonal growth to provide a "late bite." In this way some fourteen to twenty-eight days earlier grazing can be secured, with a comparable extension at the end of the season. Thus economies in feeding can be effected; for without such early and late grazing much more expensive concentrated foods, supplemented by hay, silage or dried grass, all of which are more expensive than grass which is actually grazed by the animals themselves, would be essential.

The losses of plant food from an acre of grassland which is cut three or four times in the year for silage or dried grass is likely to be equivalent to about 7-8 cwt. of sulphate of ammonia, 3 cwt. of super-phosphate and 4 cwt. of sulphate of potash. To maintain the soil at a level of fertility which will permit this standard of cropping to be carried out annually, this loss of nutrients must be made good. In districts of adequate rainfall, up to about 15 cwt. of sulphate of ammonia can be applied before the increase in the yield of herbage ceases to pay for the cost of additional fertiliser.

The practice of liming—to ensure the correct calcium status of the soil—is carried out at regular intervals, every three or four years, depending upon the type of soil and the purpose for which the grass is used. Some soils, such as those on Millstone Grit and Coal Measures, are inherently short of calcium, whereas limestone soils and calcareous clays may have a superabundance of this vital element. To-day, the loss of calcium from the soil is generally made good by periodic dressings of ground limestone applied at one to four tons per acre, frequently by a contractor using mechanical spreaders.

When deciding upon a fertiliser policy for grassland, the wise farmer has soil analyses of his grass fields carried out regularly, either by the National Agricultural Advisory Service or by the fertiliser firm. Phosphate and potash are basal dressings to ensure good clover establishment and development and optimum conditions for the growth of the good quality grasses. Nitrogen dressings are used to regulate the output of grass as desired and to time the production. Cooke quotes the following results from a recent Rothamsted experiment where S.22 Italian ryegrass was cut three times in the season for silage and a nitrogenous fertiliser was applied before each cut:

	Cwt. Dry Matter/Acre *Total 3 cuts*
No nitrogen	35
30 units nitrogen (1½ cwt. sulphate of ammonia or equivalent)	58
60 units nitrogen (3 cwt. sulphate of ammonia or equivalent)	73
90 units nitrogen (4½ cwt. sulphate of ammonia or equivalent)	78

The goal must be to blend the clovers and the grasses in the ideal proportion to permit nitrogenous fertilisers to extend the grazing season without at the same time depressing the clovers and losing Nature's cheap nitrogen. The extremes in practice can be seen in New Zealand and Holland. New Zealand farmers rely almost entirely on clover to provide nitrogen for the optimum growth of the grasses and nitrogenous fertilisers are seldom used. Dutch farmers rely almost exclusively on fertiliser nitrogen and it is unusual to find a clover sward in Holland, such as one commonly sees in this country. The plan which I think best meets the needs of mixed farming with dairy and beef cattle and sheep, is to aim at producing a sward containing 60 per cent of the really productive grasses and 40 per cent of white clover. In the course of each season a total of 6-8 cwt. per acre of nitrogenous fertiliser will be used according to need, while the phosphate and potash content of the soil will be maintained at the correct level as determined by soil analysis. It has been assumed all through this discussion that the lime requirement of the soil has been satisfied.

The moisture content of the soil is always the dominant factor in the growth of grass, which accounts for the lack of emphasis placed on the grass crop in the drier, eastern half of England compared with the west and south-west. The limitation to grass growth caused by lack of water is very apparent in periods of drought when, even in the high rainfall areas, grass fields may become parched. An adequate supply of water is essential not only to secure the maximum overall yield of herbage but also to maintain a constant rate of growth during the summer, and thereby overcome the mid-season decline which is common in many districts. Moreover, the maximum response to fertilisers cannot be obtained if the water supply is inadequate.

The high water table found in many parts of the Netherlands ensures a level production of grass during the growing season and maximum response to fertiliser applications, and is in marked contrast to the spasmodic growth secured in this country, where we rely, in the main, solely on rainfall. More and more of our leading grass farmers, therefore, are considering irrigation.

Irrigation of farm crops is a very ancient practice. Recent excavations at Jericho indicate it was carried on there 7,000 years ago, and the remains of water tanks have been discovered which were used for this purpose 3,000 years before the Pyramids were built. The Romans used irrigation extensively but it is doubtful if they introduced it to this country.

The flooding of water meadows was fairly widely practised after the seventeenth century and can still occasionally be seen to-day. This low-lying land is regularly irrigated by the river or stream running alongside it, when it floods during the winter after heavy rains or snow. This is a natural process and when the water subsides a deposit of silt is left on the grassland which has considerable fertilising value. To regulate the flooding, however, embankment and the construction of sluices and irrigation channels is necessary. The improvement in the amount of herbage produced on these meadows is very noticeable and in all likelihood is due as much to the nutrients which the flood waters supply as to the water itself. Owing to difficulties associated with grazing wet land these water meadows were finally mown for hay. Most of them have fallen into disuse now, sluices and channels are neglected and derelict and the grassland is used for grazing.

In the early 1930's, experimental work on irrigation was instituted at Jealott's Hill Research Station and this was begun again in 1949, with the object of finding out when to irrigate, and how much water to apply. A 27 per cent increase in the yield of dry matter was obtained with irrigation only, but when this was linked to applications of nitrogenous fertiliser the increase rose to 83 per cent. The value of irrigation cannot, however, be assessed only on a basis of increased yield of herbage. The timing of production is even more important for, if a farmer can ensure the growth of grass during a period of drought and thus avoid the necessity for having to feed expensive purchased foods to his stock in order to maintain production, or even growth, the value under these circumstances of this "emergency grass" may be far in excess of its commercial value as grass.

The application of water as "artificial rain" rather than by means of furrows or channels dates from the nineteen-twenties when perforated pipes, carried on stands above the crop, were oscillated by means of simple motors or even by hand. Modern equipment now used in many parts of the world consists of sprinkler-nozzles mounted on a rotating head. Rain-guns, working on the same principle but on a much larger scale, are used for large farms, and one rain-gun can water at least an acre of ground from one position.

A supply of cheap water is essential to make irrigation an economic proposition for grassland. The practice is confined, therefore, to farms which are fortunate enough to have a stream or river running through them or can obtain cheap water by boring.

All these factors which affect growth, such as fertilising and irrigation, must be carefully co-ordinated with the time of cutting or grazing to ensure that the rate of herbage growth is maintained at the highest level. The optimum area of leaf must be exposed to the light if photosynthesis is to be exploited to the full and maximum crop production obtained. Grassland management should be such that the leaf area is maintained at near the optimum level for as long as possible throughout the growing season. The whole of this complex problem is concerned with the concept of leaf area index (L.A.I.) which can be defined as the area of leaf per unit area of ground. Research work in Australia and elsewhere has shown that as the L.A.I. increases with the regrowth of leaves following cutting or grazing, photosynthesis per unit area of leaf falls off. However, it falls initially more slowly than the L.A.I. increases, so that there is an optimum L.A.I. at which photosynthesis per unit area of ground is greatest for that particular time of year. The L.A.I. will rise above the optimum until a maximum level is reached at which the production of new leaves just balances the dying-off of the lower completely shaded leaves. The aim must be to strike the right balance and in the Australian experiments swards which were cut to a height of five inches had higher growth rates for thirty-two days after cutting than had the swards which were cut to one inch or three inches. It would appear from this work, therefore, that the aim of the grazier should be lenient rotational grazing, in which the sward is never completely bared to the ground and where there is always some green herbage left for photosynthesis. On the other hand, at the Grassland Research Institute the highest total yield of herbage over the season has been obtained by cutting every eight weeks to one inch. It is clear that a good deal more work is needed on this very complex problem before precise instructions for cutting or grazing can be given to the farmer. For the present, practical experience will stand the farmer in good stead. Some of our leading grass farmers are already securing quite astonishingly high yields of milk from their grassland by a skilful blending of the principles of good management which we have enumerated in detail. It is possible by the use of sensible seeds mixtures, maximum fertiliser application, tightly-controlled grazing, and the interplay of grazing animals and forage harvester, to obtain an output of nine hundred gallons of milk per acre. There are still far too many acres of indifferent grassland. The immense untapped wealth in our grassland constitutes a vast task which confronts not only advisory officers, but also politicians and the planners of our economy.

CHAPTER 12

TOOLS AND THE GRASSLAND FARMER

The earliest known cultivating tools were the knife and the sickle. Stone knives were used by the Australian aborigines and it is likely that in Europe neolithic man used a crescent-shaped piece of flint as a sickle. Serrated flint flakes set in a straight wooden shaft were used by the earliest cultivators in Egypt, while in neolithic Britain a large flake of flint was set at right-angles in a socket at the end of a wooden shaft. Bronze sickles, to be seen in many museums, were used during the Bronze Age and these were followed by curved, hook-like, iron sickles in the Early Iron Age. Although known to the Greeks, the scythe was a much later invention than the sickle, and is still in use. Modern cutting is done by machines which are very versatile, cheap, and easy to operate. These have now displaced the hand tools for all jobs except on small farms or in cases where grass needs to be mown on inaccessible sites. The Swiss, for instance, on many small farms still scythe grass from the hillside and cart it in wheelbarrows to their cows, which may be housed even in summer.

Another early tool was the brush harrow—simply brushwood, preferably thorns, fixed on a wooden frame and dragged over the ground, first by man, and later by oxen or horses, to spread molehills and animal droppings. This was the forerunner of the flexible chain harrow used on every farm until recent times. It became increasingly evident, however, that more drastic treatment was needed on much of our grassland. Old herbage needs to be pulled out and the soil aerated and stirred. This necessitated fitting sharp turf-blades or tines on to the chain harrow, which actually dig into the ground as the harrow is hauled across the field. When cross-harrowing is considered necessary the grass field may be so churned up as to appear almost like arable land, yet the new grass appears fresh and green. Unfortunately, if there is much dead material to be pulled up, the turf-cutting tines soon become clogged and instead of cutting into the soil ride on top of

PLATE 9. Sheep grazing. *Above*, the highlands and moorlands of Britain, as here in Glen Clunie, Aberdeenshire, often support large flocks of sheep which adapt themselves to the poorer types of herbage. *Below*, orchard land, being difficult to cultivate, is often grassed

PLATE 10. Grazing for beef cattle. *Above*, Red Devons (Red Rubies) in their native county. *Below*, Herefords

it. Cleaning the tines by hand naturally slows down the work and adds considerably to the cost of the operation. Self-cleaning devices have therefore been developed and these work most efficiently. Also used under certain conditions are rotary cultivators which can be set to work about three inches deep, and which cut the turf into small pieces. Such an operation is generally followed by harrowing and rolling, and seeds and fertilisers are often applied.

Seed was first sown by hand; in the case of grass seeds a pinch of seed was taken between the thumb and first fingers from a hopper or basket carried in front and slung from the shoulders. This was broadcast using a wide sweeping action of the arm moving rhythmically from right to left. Some workers could broadcast using both hands, others were less skilled. To aid even distribution, it was not uncommon to mix the seed with dry powdered earth or sand, as it is much simpler to effect an even cover with a large amount of material.

The task of hand sowing was greatly speeded up when the fiddle drill was invented. This simple tool enabled small seeds to be scattered evenly over the ground by adopting the easy sawing motion of the fiddler with his bow. The fiddle is replaced by a knapsack holding the seed and the bow operates a reciprocating tray on to which the seeds fall. The fiddle drill may be slow in the hands of a novice but when used by a skilled operator it is speedy and gives a very even distribution. It is certainly invaluable on hillsides or broken ground where a seed drill could not be used. Good work, however, is dependent on a still day, for in windy weather some seeds may be blown considerable distances.

Many grain drills can be adapted to sow grass seeds and a drill is undoubtedly the best machine to use for normal purposes as it ensures even distribution of the seed, which is placed below the surface of the soil in contact with the moisture needed for germination. On large farms a special small-seeds drill may be used. This consists of a long seed box with a brush feed, the whole being mounted direct on to the tractor. The machine which is specially designed for sowing grass and clover seeds gives a better performance than a general-purpose machine, which can only be a compromise.

Fertiliser drills of widely varying type have for long been part of the equipment of the grassland farmer. Broadcasting by hand is a slow and messy job and agricultural engineers soon devised a more expeditious and accurate method of distribution. The latest fertiliser equipment injects liquid fertiliser direct into the soil and this operation can be carried out by contractors. A good deal of experimental work

G.G.   H is necessary before one can say whether this process has significant advantages over the more orthodox forms of distribution, and we have yet to prove the superiority of liquid fertiliser over the older granular or powder forms. The indications are that the liquid fertiliser is much quicker in action, while the convenience of having the work carried out by a contractor often justifies the extra cost. Incidentally, spraying for weeds is also likely to be carried out on a co-operative basis, except on the larger farms which carry their own equipment.

The most important job which machinery has to perform for grassland is that of mowing the grass. Climate is always a hazard, and equally important, grass only remains at the peak of its feeding value for a brief spell of time. Mowing must therefore be carried out quickly and efficiently and the choice of the appropriate machine to suit the specific conditions of any particular farm is most important. The choice of mower is wide, but most machines, even on the very small farms, are operated through the power take-off shaft from the tractor and are mounted on the hydraulically controlled links. These machines are extremely versatile, easy to operate under a wide range of con- ditions, and most reliable. Maintenance is largely confined to keeping the knife sections sharp and in good order.

A wide range of equipment is available for hay-making. Swath turners and side-delivery rakes turn the cut grass over to promote drying, while tedders and kickers toss the grass into the air to speed up the drying process still further. To collect together the dry hay when it is ready for carting and stacking, various types of hay rake are available. Some of these machines are dual, others triple, purpose.

The method of collecting the dry hay will depend largely on the distance between the crop and the point at which it is to be stacked. For long hauls from the field to the barns or stackyard, carts, wagons or trailers will be used, and to facilitate loading the hay from the ground into the transport vehicle mechanical loaders may be used. When the hay is to be stacked in the field, however, hay sweeps with long, metal-tipped wooden teeth are attached to the tractor and driven along a windrow of hay until a sufficient load has been collected on the teeth. (Originally this work was done by a pair of horses with a purely wooden sweep.) The sweep, complete with its load of hay, is then driven to the stack. The tractor is put into reverse for a few yards, to leave the pile of hay on the ground, and elevators are likely to be used to lift the hay from the ground on to the stack, although grabs and pole-loaders are also employed.

An even commoner method is to use a pick-up baler. The

mechanism consists of rotating spring tines which pick up the hay from the ground and throw it on to a conveyor which carries it to the baling chamber where it is compressed into a block, tied automatically with twine or wire, and then ejected on to the field. It remains for the bales to be picked up, put on trailers, and carted home. Many farmers use sledges attached behind the baler to collect the bales, thus saving time collecting bales dropped all over the field. A wide range of balers is available, the choice of type being largely a matter of personal preference.

The pick-up baler can also be used for silage making when bales of fresh grass are carted to the silo instead of the loose grass which is more commonly carted. For loose grass the buckrake—steel-tined sweep— was by far the commonest tool used. Within the last five years, however, forage harvesters have become the principal tools for collecting grass for silage making. This is largely the result of American experience with the maize crop which, over there, is more commonly grown for silage than is grass. Maize for silage must first be chopped and since labour is much scarcer in the United States than it is in this country, the whole process of making silage is mechanised. Forage harvesters are of two types, one in which the forage is cut and chopped with a reciprocating knife and cutter bar, and the other, which makes use of steel arms revolving at high speed on a horizontal bar. The latter slashes or tears the grass away as distinct from the cutting action of the former. The shattered material is blown into accompanying trailers or self-unloading wagons. Blowers or elevators are again used for filling the silos. Although self-feeding of silage, the cows helping themselves to the silage from the clamp, is commonly practised on the larger farms in this country, in the United States electrically-operated unloaders and conveyors are used which form an integral part of tower silos. This idea is being tried out on a number of farms and experimental stations in this country but however efficient it may prove to be, the great capital outlay required must make it unacceptable to the majority of farmers over here.

Only very recently has the problem of work study received much attention in connection with farm practice in this country. However, the importance of the efficient handling of foodstuffs is now becoming widely appreciated not only by farmers but, more important perhaps, by those responsible for research and development, and particularly by the manufacturers of farm equipment. It is likely, therefore, that in the near future we shall see quite revolutionary changes in our methods of conservation. In the U.S.A., for instance, one manufacturer has produced a baler which makes square bales of hay or partially dried grass which are then catapulted into a trailer in which the bales roll automatically into position. Other manufacturers are evolving machines to "pellet" or "wafer" the hay. The wafers are two to four inches in diameter, about half an inch thick, and are eaten readily by cattle. Progress is likely to be rapid from now on and in the years ahead we are likely to make much better use of grass conserved as hay or silage than we have done in the past.

CHAPTER 13

THE CONSERVATION OF GRASS

By far the simplest and cheapest way of feeding herbivorous animals is to let them help themselves to an adequate supply of good grass, and the ways and means of accomplishing this have been discussed in chapter 10. Unfortunately, however, grass does not grow in this country during the winter months for a period of time which varies according to climate, soil and situation. The climate is also too harsh for other than the hardiest cattle and sheep and the rainfall especially when allied to a heavy clay soil means that grazing by stock brings about much mechanical damage to the turf and possible harm to the soil structure, which is called in farming terms "poaching." Thus to maintain stock over the winter feeding period provision must be made to conserve some of summer's bountiful grass harvest in the form of hay, dried grass, or silage. In the season 1957/8 in the United Kingdom, 5,677,000 acres of grass both permanent and temporary were cut for hay, yielding an average of 25·4 cwt. of hay per acre.

Fresh grass contains about 80 per cent of moisture and if this is reduced to no more than 15 to 20 per cent the material is sufficiently dry to prevent the formation of moulds and it can then be stored in stacks or barns until it is required for feeding. The original method, known as haymaking, of drawing off the surplus moisture by using sun and wind is practised the world over. In our climate this is a hazardous business, for showers of rain not only lengthen the process and add to its costliness, but cause loss of soluble nutrients within the herbage. Indeed, as in the summer of 1965, the weather may be so adverse that complete loss of crop results.

One solution to this problem is to pass the grass through a heated chamber to produce dried grass, which is then stored in bales, or ground into meal and stored in paper bags until required for feeding. This is the most efficient method of conservation, for only water is lost from the grass, but it is also the most expensive method. As a result only about 969 farms were drying grass in 1957 in England and Wales and the total production was of the order of 110,000 tons.

The ideal compromise between the cheap, but risky, method of haymaking and the expensive, but safe, method of grass drying lies in the conversion of the fresh grass into silage.

To make hay, the grass is allowed to grow through the spring and early summer until the flowering heads appear, without being cultivated or grazed by stock. At this stage it reaches the maximum weight of herbage per acre without the plants becoming very fibrous, which they do when seed is set. The feeding value of the grass, as we have seen, resides in the leaf and not the stem, and hence a leafy hay is a much more valuable feeding stuff than hay made from a stemmy, mature crop. The ideal time for cutting is usually around early June, though unfortunately the common tendency is to err on the late side. In broad outline the process is the same wherever practised, though the details may differ from district to district, being governed to a great extent by rainfall.

The crop is cut by a mowing machine, which leaves the grass lying in rows or swaths, and these are not touched until the upper surface is dry. The swaths are then turned over to allow the undersurface to dry, when the herbage can be collected up and either carted home loose for stacking, or baled in the field. The swaths may be tossed into the air to fluff the herbage up so speeding up the drying process; and in districts of low rainfall the modern practice is to do this immediately on mowing, which may save twenty-four hours or more in the time taken to "make" the hay. Such a procedure increases the risk of spoilage by rain, for the fluffed-up grass is more easily wetted than when lying in a compact swath, and this makes it too risky a procedure in districts of high rainfall. Where the weather in summer is unreliable, the hay is collected, when about half-made, into heaps known as "cocks" or "pikes," to complete its drying gradually. In this way less surface area is exposed to wet weather and the risks of spoilage or even loss of crop are thereby lessened. In districts of high rainfall even these precautions may be of little avail and then the hay is hung on tripods or poles, or even wire fencing, to dry in the same way that the domestic clothes are hung on the line. This is a common method in the Scandinavian and mid-European countries where small farms are frequent.

The sun is a powerful bleaching and drying agency and in very hot sunny weather care must be taken to avoid getting the crop over dry, for then the leaf is liable to be broken off in the field while the hay is being gathered up, and a stalky, stemmy hay of low feeding value results. Bleached hay is undesirable, for then the valuable carotene, which is a constituent of the chlorophyll complex and the precursor of Vitamin A is lost. On the other hand, care must be taken to see that the hay is really "fit" before carting. If too much sap is left in the stems, or surface moisture has not been completely evaporated, sweating and moulding will occur in the barn or the stack and a musty hay results which is rejected by stock. When an immature hay is carted, fermentation in the stack follows, heating takes place, and the valuable proteins may be rendered indigestible and useless. In serious cases of over-heating the hay may even burst into flames by spontaneous combustion. The process of hay-making, therefore, is not quite so simple as it would appear.

Modern technique enables hay to be made in three days—indeed with good drying conditions in forty-eight hours—and this minimum spell of good weather can generally be ensured by working in conjunction with the Meteorological Office's fine-spell forecasting service. To achieve this speed, the mowing machine is followed by a crimping machine which passes the swath of grass through a pair of fluted steel rollers, cracking the stems and squeezing out the sap so that the stems—which are normally very difficult to dry—cure as quickly as the leaf. The tedding machine and turner follow when the upper surfaces are dry, and finally the baler makes the crop ready for carting.

The comparative inefficiency of the haymaking process gave rise in the late 1930's to the development of grass drying, whereby air, heated by means of coke, by oil-burning furnaces, or by electricity, drives off the surplus moisture. Quite apart from the complete absence of risk from adverse weather, artificial drying has the additional advantage that it can continue from early spring to late autumn using young, short grass of maximum feeding value, whereas haymaking can only commence when the grasses have reached the flowering stage for prior to this it is not possible to handle the crop efficiently enough in the field for natural drying to take place. Such grass can be dried effectively to produce a concentrated food replacing purchased concentrates in meat or milk production. The meal is purchased by the compounders of cattle foods for inclusion in their mixtures. It is also particularly valuable in poultry foods. A development which has taken place in Denmark recently is likely to be more widely adopted. The grass is harvested and chopped into one inch lengths before being dried. It is then immediately made into cubes 1 ×2 inches, known as "briquettes," which are used for feeding to dairy cows during the winter. The product is more palatable than grass meal.

The chief advantages of artificial drying are, therefore, that it is independent of weather conditions and that the final product is of high feeding value. The drawback is that special equipment must be installed, which is expensive, and the cost of operation is high, which makes the final product dear, too dear for the average farm.

More and more farmers to-day are effecting a compromise by installing barn hay-driers. These are cheaper to instal and enable cold or hot air—whichever is required—to be blown through the hay, which is already stacked in the barn. This hay may be carted earlier than would otherwise be feasible—thus reducing the risk of weather damage—and the drying is comparatively cheap. Rather more mature grass is used, with a correspondingly lower moisture content and the process is more leisurely, so that labour costs are reduced and the drying can be carried out for long periods without attention —and even during "off peak" periods, when cheap current is available. What is more, it is possible to instal machines with the dual function of hay drying or grain drying, which reduces overhead costs very appreciably.

The installation is relatively simple. The floor of the barn is over-laid with an openwork floor or system of air ducts which may be constructed of brick, metal, or wood, and this area is enclosed on the four sides with a reasonably air-tight wall running to the full height of the barn. This chamber is then connected with the power fan in such a way that hot air or cold air can be blown into the base of the drying chamber and up through the hay which is stacked on top of the openwork floor.

The crop is cut and wilted to about 60 per cent moisture which, as we have already seen, is a simple matter, given a few hours of good weather. It is then carted to the drier and loaded on to the perforated floor to a height of about six to eight feet, drying proceeding all the time that loading is taking place. When the first load is partially dried a further batch is put on top of the first, and then a third and fourth. Usually an initial depth of about eight feet settles to six feet. When the drier is finally filled to the top it is often left until required for feeding. If more convenient for the farmer the grass can be baled in the field with about 50 per cent moisture and then dried by blowing the air through several layers of bales at a time, gradually filling up the drying chamber in the same way as with loose hay.

Portable driers are available, which have the advantage that they can be erected in the field where the hay is being made. The bales of hay are stacked in such a manner that a tunnel is formed in the interior. The moisture extraction unit consists of a high-efficiency axial-flow fan coupled to a heavy-duty air-cooled diesel engine. The fan produces a very high volume of air, using the heat of the engine to warm it. The warm air is directed into the tunnel and passes through the bales of hay to dry them.

The alternative to hay or dried grass is silage (for a detailed description of the process see p. 108). The ancients were in the habit of storing their grain in pits and it is thought that this provides the origin of the method. The process is "ensilage," the product obtained is "silage," and the container used is the "silo," the word silo being a corruption of a Latin word "sirus" meaning "a pit."

The problem of making hay in bad weather has always been a trouble to farmers in this country, but never more so than in the exceptionally wet seasons following 1879. They were therefore ready to consider new ideas, and when, in 1882, a Frenchman, the Vicomte de Chezelles, paid a visit to the Royal Show at Reading and there gave an account of his methods of making silage in pits, great stimulus was given to the practice.

Silos of many descriptions were constructed throughout the country, the common type being the pit dug in the ground. That this type was so prevalent when experience was so limited was probably unfortunate, for unless proper care is taken in making pit silage the waste is unduly high and the product apt to be sour.

There is no doubt that bad silage was made at that time, and this fact did not help to establish the practice, while the report of a Royal Commission, appointed in 1885 to consider the possibilities of ensilage in this country, did little to advance matters. Thus in the following years the practice virtually disappeared from British farming, though a few faithful and successful adherents remained.

During this period ensilage was also introduced into North America, where it at once caught on and has continued to flourish ever since, until at the present time the majority of farms in Canada and the United States carry a tower silo. Several factors contributed to this state of affairs, the chief one undoubtedly being the adoption of the tower silo as the standard type. This silo gives a uniform product with very little waste, upkeep costs are low, and it is simple and easy to fill. Thus American farmers started on a sound basis. Moreover, maize has always been their chief silage crop. This gives a good quality product and a large and reliable yield per acre. It is also one of the simplest crops to ensile.

In spite of the undoubted waste attaching to the process as then practised in this country, some farmers still found it worth while to make silage in one way or another. In 1901, a tower silo was erected at the College Farm, Wye, and experiments were carried out with maize as the chief crop. The results, however, showed rather a high loss in feeding value.

In 1910 Mr. George Jacques erected a tower silo on his farm at Tivetshall, Norfolk, and filled it with oats and tares. This was successful, and his advocacy of the practice helped to establish it in the eastern counties. From then on it spread throughout the country, though never reaching spectacular proportions.

This mixed crop of oats and tares, often including peas or beans, was regarded as the most reliable and most suitable mixture to grow for silage. Roots, usually swedes and mangolds, were most often used for winter feeding, but where the growing of these crops was hazardous, the cereal-legume mixture for silage was an excellent substitute and occupied the same place in the crop rotation. The cost of tower silos, however, whether of wood, concrete or steel, was generally prohibitive, and the great majority of farmers were apathetic.

During the 1930's radical changes were made in the process, and at the outbreak of war in 1939 the stage was set for a rapid expansion of ensilage on farms throughout the country. By then it was realised that silage offers a certainty of winter keep: a protein-rich succulent food, from a variety of summer green crops, that is capable of putting bloom on the stock and of toning them up; a food which does not deteriorate in storage and is ready for feeding as required. So great has been the increase in silage production that whereas in 1940 about 250,000 tons were made, by 1957 no less than 3,860,000 tons were produced in the United Kingdom. Figures are not available for Scotland, but in England and Wales some 39,000 farmers were making it and nearly 3,000 in Northern Ireland.

To make silage the crop is cut and carted while still green and is packed tightly in the pit, tower or stack silo in order to exclude air from the mass. The plant material immediately begins to warm up, first through the continued respiration of its cells, and then, as these die, through the rapid growth of micro-organisms carried on the greenstuff. Provided that air is excluded by tight packing the particular micro-organisms which are able to develop will be those that attack carbohydrates to produce organic acids, mainly lactic (the acid in sour milk). Lactic acid prevents the growth of undesirable putrefactive bacteria, and so acts as a preservative. The material by this time is silage and will keep indefinitely, provided air is kept out. Crops which are very rich in protein and low in carbohydrate, clover, lucerne or young grass for example, are ensiled with the addition of molasses to ensure that adequate carbohydrate is available for the micro-organisms to produce the essential lactic acid. In Scandinavia, preservation is secured by spraying on a weak acid solution (usually a mixture of hydrochloric and sulphuric acids sold as A.I.V. acid) while in other parts of Europe, formic acid is used. In America, sodium meta-bisulphite powder is sprinkled over the herbage, this chemical apparently inhibiting the activity of the micro-organisms.

Vacuum silage is a method of making silage very recently intro-duced, in which the fermentation losses are cut to the absolute minimum by creating anaerobic conditions immediately, and hence a product of higher feeding value is obtained.

In normal silage most of the dry matter losses occur through the oxidation of the carboyhdrates present in the greenstuff to carbon dioxide and water, and the extent of the dry matter loss (and hence food value) depends on the amount of oxygen present in, and diffusing into, the ensiled crop.

When anaerobic conditions are created immediately the carbo-hydrates will be converted only to organic acids, lowing the pH and eventually stopping further bacterial growth. This means that the carbohydrates are utilised more efficiently and there is no need to add molasses to crops rich in protein which would require them with normal silage-making methods.

In this method the fresh herbage is packed as quickly as possible into a polythene or rubber envelope or container, which when filled is sealed to make it airtight and is then connected to a pump which exhausts the air and effects the required anaerobic conditions.

Much further experimental work is necessary before the full advantages—or disadvantages—of the method are completely under-stood. It would seem at the moment to be a promising method for development since the saving in food value of the herbage will probably be greater than the increased costs involved.

Another development in America, that of making haylage, has recently been given trial in this country. Haylage can most simply be described as a product half-way between hay and silage. The green crop is cut and allowed to wilt in the field down to a moisture content of 40 to 60 per cent. The crop is then chopped and blown into a tower silo constructed of steel with a glass lining which is made completely airtight by using marine-type self-sealing filler hatches. Thus oxygen is excluded, respiration of the plant cells and anaerobic organisms reduced to a minimum, and the haylage is preserved as a result of the development of anaerobic conditions, the relative lack of moisture and the presence of organic acids produced by micro-organisms from the carbohydrates in the fodder. Filling can be continuous and the haylage can be used as and when needed by an automatic feeding device which churns the fodder out from the bottom or the top of the airtight silos. The product is sweet-smelling and well liked by stock. A number of farmers have erected these silos in this country but it is too early, as yet, to draw conclusions as to the merit of haylage over good silage. Owing to the presence of carbon dioxide it is highly dangerous to enter a partially filled silo.

CHAPTER 14

ANIMAL HEALTH ON GRASSLAND

Although grass is accepted as the natural food for most types of herbivorous animals, intensive grassland management, allied to a failure to observe the rules of good husbandry, can combine to jeopardise the health of stock.

In the wake of increased grass output, brought about by very liberal fertilising and the use of new and improved strains of grasses and legumes, must come heavier rates of stocking. Inevitably, heavier stocking rates lead to parasitism, especially in sheep, where stomach and bowel worms can be a serious menace to the health of the animals, resulting in debility, perhaps to the point of death; hence the saying "a sheep's worst enemy is another sheep."

Veterinarians have made considerable progress in the development of therapeutic chemicals for the treatment of internal parasites but parasitic gastro-enteritis is still a major problem in sheep management. It is complicated by the fact that there are many types of worm affecting sheep and not all these types respond to the same treatment. This has been made abundantly clear in recent years by losses that have resulted from *Nematodirus*, a worm that will live successfully in young lambs and is capable of surviving on the pasture for twelve months. The normal system of grazing management which kept other stomach worms down to a reasonable level is quite ineffective in controlling *Nematodirus*, for ewes are not carriers of heavy infestations, unlike other types of worms, and the trouble is only prevented by grazing fresh pastures in the following year. Should this not be feasible then at least one must avoid putting lambs on suspect fields during the critical months of April to June.

For economic returns very high stocking rates are essential and the grass should be consumed when young and leafy and highly nutritious. This has led to various devices to permit creep grazing, giving the lambs access to the pasture ahead of the ewes, being incorporated into grazing systems. In the "forward" system, creeps are used through which lambs pass to graze ahead of their mothers whereas in "sideways" creep grazing the lambs are maintained on a constant, highly nutritious diet of young leafy swards without competition from the ewes. Not only does the nutritional advantage strengthen the resistance of the lambs to worm infestation but there is a reduction in the uptake of infective material since it is the lower regions of the sward which are most heavily infected. The ewes ensure the complete pasture defoliation which is essential for the uniform recovery of the sward to provide the next crop of grass.

Heavy applications of potash and nitrogenous fertilisers are sometimes associated with a condition in cattle known as hypomagnesæmia ("grass tetany," "grass staggers," or "Hereford disease") where abnormally low concentrations of magnesium in the blood bring about sudden death. The disease may have been recognised first in Hereford but is now experienced in all parts of the country. Many farmers are conversant with the symptoms of restlessness, twitching of the muscles, excitable behaviour, and staggering gait which are followed by convulsions and death if treatment is not given at once. The problem is not due simply to the magnesium in the soil being locked up by the excessive use of potash and nitrogen, leading to a low magnesium content in the herbage, but to a much more complicated physiological effect. Cold weather may bring on an attack. The use of fertilisers, which have a high content of magnesium, such as dolomitic limestone, may help to prevent the trouble, but cannot be relied upon to do so. However, provided the additional expense is not too great their use as a precautionary measure is worthwhile. In cases where the soil does not need lime—and rectifying the deficiency through the medium of the soil is a long-term project—it is usual to feed to cattle and sheep calcined magnesite which contains up to 55 per cent of magnesium.

The use of intensively fertilised and rapidly grown herbage, especially in the spring of the year, may cause "bloat" ("hoven" or "rumen tympany") in cattle. This condition, in which the animal fails to eructate and liberate the gas formed in the rumen by the fermenting green fodder, results in the animal's body being greatly distended or "blown" in the region of the left flank. Respiratory distress follows from pressure on the chest and, in acute cases, death may occur if remedial treatment is not immediately administered. In fact the animal literally "blows up." In really acute cases, death may occur within an hour or two of the stock eating lush grass and clover or frosted food. Cases of severe distention must be treated immediately and the accumulation of gas causing the trouble released by puncturing the animal in the affected region. In emergencies a knife can be used, but the veterinary surgeon uses a trocar and cannula. If the bloat is caused by frothy material, gas is trapped in the fermenting food and simple puncturing may not give relief. Silicones and other agents which reduce surface tension can, in less severe cases, be administered by mouth.

The prevention of bloat is in some cases a simple matter of husbandry. When cattle or sheep are put on to rich young pastures they should first be given a feed of hay or straw so that the inclination to gorge themselves is removed. Another simple expedient is to limit the time they are allowed to graze such herbage or restrict the amount available by using a movable electric fence.

"Husk," characterised by severe coughing, is a condition which affects young cattle in the autumn when grazing on pastures seriously infected with the lung worm or husk worm, a fine threadlike worm which lives in the air passages in the lungs and causes bronchitis, and sometimes death. Sheep also suffer from husk but those chiefly affected are lambs during their first winter. The species of lung worms are different from those affecting cattle, but the symptoms of attack and the control measures to be adopted are similar. A vaccine is now available to give protection and affected animals should be removed from the pasture and given supplementary concentrate foods.

Silage has often been blamed for taints in milk. In days gone by when cows were milked by hand into open buckets, the complaint was justified if the silage was fed just before milking. Then the rather heavy, clinging type of odour associated with silage, especially when badly made, was absorbed by the milk. The simple expedient of feeding the silage after milking instead of before usually cleared up this trouble. When, however, failure to observe the rules of good silage-making results in the production of butyric acid, an evil-smelling and -tasting substance resembling rancid butter at its worst, it may be absorbed by the animal system, to reappear in the milk, causing serious tainting. It is not uncommon for churns of milk to be rejected by commercial dairies on this account.

There is also a firmly-rooted opinion, with some evidence to support it, that feeding large quantities of silage, especially when it is made from young, immature and very succulent herbage, tends to a decline in the solids-not-fat (s.n.f.) content of milk. This is important because the law states that if the s.n.f. content falls below 8·50 per cent it is presumed, until the contrary is proved, that the milk is not as it came from the cow. On the other hand, the prejudice voiced by some butchers against silage-fed beef cannot be substantiated, for there is no evidence of any undesirable taste or any other defect in the flesh of silage-fed animals.

Bovine infertility is another problem which has been causing concern. There is considerable evidence that the nutritional status of the animal is associated with delayed breeding. Since the majority of cows in this country are mated during the grazing season it is essential for the pasture to supply the nutrients required—protein, carbohydrates, vitamins and minerals—in adequate amount. Of the minerals, calcium and phosphorus are especially important. In South Africa, and in many other countries where the soil is naturally deficient in phosphorus, reports indicate a direct relationship between this deficiency and delayed breeding in cows and heifers.

Cobalt and copper deficiency in pasture land may also account for disease in the grazing animal. For example, a condition known as "pining"—a most descriptive name—of sheep and cattle is common in Scotland, northern England, and Wales and is due to shortage of cobalt, while in Derbyshire a lack of copper in the grassland is associated with "swayback" in sheep. The former can be prevented by applying cobalt direct to the pasture, administering it in suitable form to the animal direct, or more simply by turning the animals on to a piece of normal pasture. "Swayback"—again most descriptive—affects young lambs at or within three months of birth and the copper is best supplied in a mineral lick to the pregnant ewe.

It is interesting to note that while absence of essential minerals may give rise to diseases, excess of a particular mineral may be equally troublesome. There is, for instance, the case of the "teart" pastures of Somerset in which the clovers for some reason contain an excess of molybdenum. Cattle and calves are chiefly affected but sometimes sheep may be also. Affected animals have staring coats and a general appearance of unthriftiness in contrast to the shining, sleek appearance of thriving stock. They may suffer from acute and persistent diarrhoea and even waste away. Fertilising which increases the yield of herbage often effects some control of the trouble, for while increasing the amount of grass, it does not increase the amount of molybdenum absorbed by the clovers, and thus brings about a dilution of concentration and reduces the degree of "teartness" of the pasture. An allowance of 2 gr. of copper sulphate daily, either in the drinking water or with the food, is the best control measure known and it would seem, therefore, that the ratio of copper to molybdenum is important. Hay made

PLATE 11. *Above left*, a grass dominant sward. *Right*, an ideal combination of grass and clover. *Below*, perfect food for all herbivorous stock at its highest feeding value

PLATE 12. Traditional methods. *Above*, raking and cocking hay in Essex. *Below*, carting hay near Llanrwst, Denbighshire

from these "teart" fields produces the same symptoms as the herbage itself unless it is more than a year old.

Many bacterial diseases of animals can be transmitted from infected to healthy stock when contaminated grass is eaten. The tubercle bacillus, for instance, can live for at least a month after being excreted in the dung of an infected animal on to a pasture. During the winter it may even live for five months. Germs in the sputum and urine are equally dangerous. Contagious abortion can be transmitted in the same fashion. The discharge from an animal which has just aborted may infect a pasture for three months and if the decomposing fœtus or fœtal membranes are not destroyed at once the contamination may be of longer duration. Another wasting condition is due to Johne's disease, the bacillus of which has been known to be infective for 246 days after being voided in the excretion of an infected animal. So far as anthrax is concerned, the bacterial spores live in soil for many years but fortunately the virus of the dreaded foot-and-mouth disease loses its potency in about six weeks, although hay made from the same field will remain infective for as long as fifteen weeks.

In the case of all infected pastures sunshine is a powerful agent in killing organisms, and harrowing to spread the dung and allow the sunshine to penetrate into it is helpful. Dung from cattle yards carrying infected stock should never, of course, be used on grassland but always applied to arable land.

While techniques to increase grass output cause animal health problems, neglect can be equally serious. The presence of rough vegetation greatly increases the risk from blow-fly and tick-borne diseases. Fortunately dipping with organo-phosphorus compounds now provides considerable protection from blow-fly and the introduction into dips of organo-phosphorus compounds specifically designed to control ticks has also led to some improvement.

Badly drained grassland provides ideal conditions for the snail that is the alternate host to the liver-fluke which infests both cattle and sheep. Drainage and treatment of the ground with copper-sulphate can in certain cases break the life cycle of the fluke. Red water in cattle is also associated with rough grazing, wet ground and the presence of scrub.

Warble fly damage is common on cattle in this country. It causes considerable loss in the form of hides, damaged meat, and unthriftiness. New chemicals based on organo-phosphorus which are either given in the form of a compulsory drink (drench) or applied to the backs of the cattle in the autumn may be the solution to the problem.

Pigs in this country are generally managed intensively on an indoor system. However, because of the advantages of outdoor management some are kept outside, and are thus exposed to the parasitic diseases peculiar to outdoor management. For example, lung worms require the presence of earth worms to complete their life cycle. Pig-sick pastures may contain infected earth worms for anything up to four years after the pigs have been removed.

The tonic value of grass is well known and in many cases of intensive indoor management, unthrifty stock have been transformed by the addition of small amounts of dried grass to the diet. Young pigs, for instance, when reared out of doors, receive from the grass and the soil the iron and other minerals that are present in insufficient amounts in sows' milk. If it were not for the difficulties of outdoor management all piglets could be reared without risk of anæmia. Clearly grass possesses some properties which cannot yet be adequately defined by chemical analyses.

Sufficient has been said to indicate the need for skilled grassland management. By the full use of technical knowledge, particularly in the light of recent research, grass and animal can be attuned to modern demands for the maximum output of milk or meat at the minimum cost. The latter essential factor for successful farming can only be achieved, needless to say, when the stock are maintained in a fully healthy condition. They are then able to make full use of the greater quantity of grass of higher feeding value produced by modern techniques, and losses from deaths or poor condition are eliminated.

CHAPTER 15

THE MEASUREMENT OF GRASSLAND OUTPUT

Grass is acknowledged as a crop by only a minority of farmers in this country, although this minority represents the cream of the farming community, the most skilled and highly efficient. The reason for this most probably lies in the fact that grass is a perennial crop. At the end of the growing season there is a rest period during the winter months when growth is at a minimum or may cease completely. Then with the first warm, sunny days of spring, growth recommences with renewed vigour without any effort on the part of man and this cycle can continue season after season. Grass fields vary a great deal throughout the country, between north and south, east and west, and indeed grass fields on the same farm may differ. It is far from easy for the ordinary farmer to measure this variation, be it in quantity or quality of grass. Grass must first be put through the animal system before productivity can be known. By contrast, it is simplicity itself to measure and compare the yields of beet, potatoes, or cereals expressed in the tangible form of tons per acre. Of course yields of dried grass or hay can easily be determined but very few fields have the whole output for one season made into hay or dried grass.

COW GRAZING DAYS

The simplest measure of the output of grass from a field is expressed in "cow grazing days." This involves recording the number of cows— or "cow equivalents"—grazing a particular field and the number of days they graze. The result of the simple sum $\dfrac{\text{cows} \times \text{days}}{\text{acres}}$ is the output of the field expressed in cow grazing days. If the same procedure is adopted for any other field on the farm, or other fields in the county, or on a nation-wide basis, a comparative measure of production is obtained.

The simplicity of the procedure has decided appeal, but there are a number of limiting factors which greatly reduce the value of the answer obtained. In the first place, all the livestock used must be expressed in terms of some standard unit which is normally a cow grazing day. In the report of a detailed study of the problems of grassland recording the following conversion factors were adopted:

TABLE 8. TO CONVERT CATTLE OF DIFFERENT AGES TO THEIR COW EQUIVALENT

Age	Factor
Over 30 months	1·0
21-30 months	0·75
11-20 months	0·50
under 11 months	0·25

The use of these factors is satisfactory where the intention is to compare pasture output on different fields on the same farm but where different farms are being compared it is necessary to make a further correction for variation in breed. Different breeds vary in weights and therefore in the amount of grass they require; for example much less grass is required by a Jersey than a Friesian cow so a given pasture would carry more Jersey than Friesian cows. For this reason the concept of a standard cow equivalent has been introduced and is defined as the amount of bulk feed that a 1,000 lb. lactating cow will consume in 24 hours.

TABLE 9. FACTORS FOR CORRECTING COW DAYS TO STANDARD COW EQUIVALENT

Breed	Liveweight	Factor
Jersey	800 lb.	0·8
Guernsey	900 lb.	0·9
Ayrshire	1110 lb.	1·1
Friesian	1300 lb.	1·3

It is frequently the practice to keep both sheep and cattle on the same farm, using a common area of grassland. When this happens then the requirements of the sheep must also be converted to cow grazing days and possibly also to standard cow equivalents. The following table would then be used:

TABLE 10. TO CONVERT SHEEP TO COW GRAZING DAYS (The factor = *sheep/cow day*)

Liveweight range of sheep	Friesian Shorthorn	Ayrshire	Guernsey	Jersey
40— 80 lb.	14	13	11	10
80—120 lb.	10	9	8	7
120—160 lb.	7½	7	6	5
160—200 lb.	6	5½	4½	4

The choice of all the factors mentioned above was made after considering carefully a great amount of experimental evidence. Even so there are limitations to the technique. Individual animals vary enormously in their ability to convert food into useful saleable products. Moreover, the quality of the grass varies during the course of each season, from season to season and from farm to farm. However, where comparisons are being made between individual fields on the same farm the results of such calculation can show real and substantial differences in pasture production. Where this information is related to the records of fertiliser use, grazing management and type of sward, it is possible to obtain invaluable clues to methods of improving the performance of the poorer fields.

Where it is necessary to compare the grassland on different farms then the cow grazing day system, and to a lesser extent the standard cow equivalent system, encounter difficulties. On one farm a cow grazing day may refer to stock producing large quantities of milk or meat or wool and this is clearly worth much more than a cow grazing day where the animal is getting nothing but subsistence from the grass. In the latter case the farmer would be spending large sums of money on purchasing expensive concentrate foods to provide the nutrients the animals required for production. On paper the two farms may be producing the same number of cow grazing days per acre but if the financial statements of the two farms were compared at the end of the year there is no doubt which would have made more money from grass—it would most certainly be the first farm.

So far it has been assumed that all the grass produced and recorded was consumed *in situ* by grazing stock, but in practice a large proportion of the crop is often conserved for feeding in the winter. Output of hay and silage must also be credited to the fields and must, therefore, be converted to cow grazing days.

TABLE 11.   COW GRAZING DAYS PER TON OF FEED

	Friesian Shorthorn	Ayrshire	Guernsey	Jersey
Hay	68	80	97	112
Silage	21	25	30	32

To see how the system works here is an example of the utilisation of grass on a 10 acre field.

The field was:

(a)   (i) Grazed by 20 Friesian cows for 50 days;
     (ii) Grazed by 100 sheep weighing 90 lb. each for 20 days;
     (iii) Cut for hay, when quantity harvested was 10 tons.

(b) Hence the various outputs per acre during season were as follows:

(i) Cow grazing—100 Friesian cow grazing days $\dfrac{(20 \times 50)}{10}$

(ii) Sheep grazing—20 Friesian cow grazing days $\dfrac{(100 \times 20)}{10 \times 10}$

(iii) Hay   —68 Friesian cow grazing days $\dfrac{(10 \times 68)}{10}$

$$\underline{188}$$

Thus the standard cow equivalents per acre $= 188 \times 1\cdot3$ which is 244.

Many farmers are content with the rough comparison the method provides. If supplementary feeding practices and type of stock do not fluctuate widely, and a standard grazing technique is adopted, then field to field variations may be brought to light, and improvements effected on the poorest fields.

The chief merit of the system lies in its simplicity, a merit which cannot lightly be overlooked. To give an example, the following table compiled by Beynon shows how the records of 62 farms can be easily comprehended and, in spite of any limitations inherent in the method, the figures given have a definite value:

TABLE 12. COW GRAZING DAYS PER ACRE 1956/7 IN SOUTH-
WESTERN PROVINCES

11 farms out of 62 secured 100-150 cow grazing days per acre
8   250-300
3   300

This example indicates what is possible when good grass is fully utilised. The contribution made to the overall figures by grazing at different periods of the year and by conserved products is shown in the following table:

TABLE 13. COW GRAZING DAYS PER ACRE

	Dairy Farms		Cattle and Sheep Farms	
	1955/6	1956/7	1955/6	1956/7
Summer Grazing	107	109	111	121
Hay and Silage	33	36	22	22
Winter Grazing	39	41	87	96
Total production for the year	179	186	220	239

OUTPUT OF MILK AND MEAT

A further method of expressing the yield of a grass field is to record the gallons of milk per acre obtained from it. This method, unfortunately, can be interpreted in a variety of ways. The figures may be obtained by dividing the total gallonage produced by the acres devoted to milk production, with an allowance for the gallonage of milk produced from purchased feeds and non-grass foods such as kale and crops. Alternatively, the purchased concentrate food may be converted into acres (usually 1 ton to 1 acre) and the total gallonage is then divided by the total feed-acres, which is the sum of the acres devoted to livestock plus the "purchased acres." Finally, the gallons of milk produced may be stated as gallons per acre or gallons per feed-acre, which can refer to cows only or to cows and their followers. Obviously this brings about big variations in the final figures and whether cows in milk or cows plus their followers are used is generally determined by how impressive one wishes the final result to appear for obviously the first figure would be appreciably bigger than the latter. Another very big snag is that no allowance is made for density of stocking, quality of milk, or yield per cow. However, this comparatively crude method of measuring pasture production will indicate major differences. For example when visiting New Zealand a few years ago I found many farmers who secured up to 1000 gallons per acre because in that country with its wonderful climate and full reliance on grass for milk production, the general practice is to calve down when the grass is at the peak of its production in the spring. Thus cows at their peak of production enjoy the full benefit of the grass at its most nutritive and productive stage.

As with milk so with meat; pounds of meat per acre may be used as the yardstick for grassland output. Here again, great variations exist between, for example, a breeding herd with all the followers of varying ages, and store cattle bought to be finished on grass. Moreover in the latter case, the cwt./acre of meat secured is more often than not a reflection of the farmer's skill in judging a beast likely to fatten well on grass.

As a guide it may be recorded that in England 400 lb. liveweight per acre has been obtained with sheep and cattle. In Northern Ireland (1945/8) 426 to 549 lb./acre liveweight increase was secured with store cattle, and in 1953/4, 784 lb. to 692 lb. with 10 bullocks strip-grazing on 3 acres of land. Then again in Northern Ireland 45 lb.

liveweight increase for every 1 ton of grass silage fed to bullocks has been attained. If, therefore, one secures 10 tons of silage per acre—and this is by no means abnormal—it means some 450 lb. liveweight increase per acre can be produced from grassland in this way.

UTILISED STARCH EQUIVALENT

Now grass provides a number of dietary essentials—energy, protein, minerals and vitamins. For each of these it is possible to draw up a balance sheet showing how much the animals required, how much of this requirement was supplied by grass and how much was obtained from other foods. This approach to grassland recording has the advantage that tables are available to show the theoretical requirements of different stock and the composition of the foods fed in addition to the grass, so that by subtracting from the animals' needs the amounts supplied in supplementary feeds, the output of the grass is measured indirectly. Here is a simple example. If it is known that a grazing cow requires for all its needs, to maintain its body and to produce milk, 3 lb. of protein, and that it has been fed concentrates containing 1 lb. of protein, then by difference, assuming the cow has been correctly rationed, she will have obtained 2 lb. of protein from the grass. In practice, however, it is normally the contribution grass makes to the *energy* requirement of the animal that is used to measure grass production. The energy value of a food and the energy required by an animal can be measured in a number of ways. In Great Britain the custom has developed of measuring energy in terms of "starch equivalent." Starch equivalent is defined as the number of pounds of starch which would have to be fed to produce the same amount of fat that is obtained from 100 lb. of the feed.

The merits of the system are that the farmer is attempting to measure the contribution grass makes to the needs of his stock. It is unfortunate that the answer has to be obtained indirectly but this is inevitable when one cannot know either the quantity or quality of the grass consumed. Although the system may not be suitable as an experimental technique due to the assumptions inherent in it, it at least has the merit of measuring the effect of the feeding decisions that have been made during the course of the year. Moreover, it combines the requirements both for maintaining the body of the animal and for production into a single figure.

For such a calculation to be possible the farmer must know, firstly, the average number of each type of animal on the farm during the year, and secondly, the average number of days for which each of these types has been fed. Next the theoretical nutritive requirements for maintenance and production for the grazing stock must be agreed upon. For example, the standards appropriate to stock on the College farm are as follows:

Guernsey cows in milk:
for maintenance only	6 lb.	*starch equivalent per day*
for each gallon of milk produced	3 lb.	

Guernsey cow—dry and in calf	7·2 lb.
Devon cow—dry and in calf	9·6 lb.
Devon cow and calf	14·0 lb.

Young cattle:
Guernsey under 1½ years	4·8 lb.
Guernsey 1½-2¼ years	6·0 lb.
Devon under 1½ years	6·0 lb.
Devon 1½-2¼ years	7·8 lb.
Ewes: maintenance only	1·6 lb.
Ewes: last 8 weeks of pregnancy	1·9 lb.

Ewes with lambs—the total number of ewes plus lambs is multiplied by the maintenance factor, i.e. 1.6 lb. starch equivalent per day.

From these figures it is a matter of simple arithmetic to estimate the total requirement of starch equivalent for the whole farm for the whole year simply by multiplying the number of stock in each class by the starch equivalent required per day. From this total is then deducted the sum of the starch equivalent consumed in all the foods fed to the livestock *other* than grass. The balance is then ascribed to the grazing. This figure must be adjusted if there is any increase or decrease in the amounts of conserved grass at the beginning and the end of the year.

As with cow-grazing days, many assumptions and many estimates are involved. The weight of silage can be measured but its starch equivalent has to be estimated as outlined on page 122 and the figure of 11 is commonly adopted. Since most hay in these days is baled, it is a simple matter to record the number of bales made, and the average weight per bale, to give the total yield of hay produced. Early hay is likely to have a starch equivalent value of 38, whilst the late cuts would be no more than 34.

To indicate the overall situation in the country the following figures were given by the Caine Committee (*Cmnd.* 547. London).

TABLE 14. THE UTILISATION OF FEED STUFF AND LIVESTOCK REQUIREMENTS

Starch equivalent provided	*Million Tons*		
	1938/9	1950/1	1956/7
By concentrates	8·2	6·1	8·7
By grassland	12·9	13·8	14·2
By other sources including rough grazings	4·2	5·1	4·9
Total	25·3	25·0	27·8
Calculated effective usage of grass in cwt. starch equivalent per acre:	11·2	15·0	14·5

The final row of figures is of particular interest but their significance is not apparent unless it is known how the figures compare with what can be done. For example with an experiment conducted on the College farm it was possible to obtain over 23 cwt. of utilised starch equivalent per acre which is very appreciably higher than the national average while the theoretical potential is at least three times as high as the national average.

The main weakness of the method lies in the fact that differences in breeds of livestock and wastage of food are ignored. Variations in the efficiency with which stock convert food when producing at different levels are also ignored. Compared with the method of cow-grazing days, on the other hand, it has the advantage of making allowance for differences in supplementary feeding and the level of meat and milk production. Perhaps the most serious limiting factor so far as grassland is concerned, however, is that while full credit is given to all supplementary foods, the value attributed to the grass is simply the residual theoretical requirements of the stock obtained by difference.

To illustrate how the output of grassland is determined, the best procedure is to take the records of an actual farm and go through the recording stage by stage. Some figures are shown opposite. The method is that of utilised starch equivalent already referred to and standardised by the British Grassland Society. The figures relate to the period 1st October, 1959, to the 30th September, 1960.

A small proportion of the grass production came from fields utilised for only a few months, playing fields, and the like, and the total estimated utilised starch equivalent production from these fields was 213 cwt. Thus the total estimated utilised starch equivalent production from fields in grass for the whole year was: 3728−213 =3515 cwt. The total acreage of fields in grass for the whole year was

TABLE 15. GRASS PRODUCTION ON SEALE HAYNE COLLEGE FARM 1960

Estimated utilised starch equivalent production in cwt.

	Summer Period 1 Apr.—30 Sep.		Winter Period 1 Oct.—31 Mar.		Whole Year 1 Oct.—30 Sep.	
	Total	%	Total	%	Total	%
Utilised by						
Zero grazing cows	395	13	—	—	395	11
Other dairy cows	485	16	7	1	492	13
Sheep	826	26	417	67	1243	33
Beef cows and calves	325	10	158	25	483	13
Young cattle	247	8	40	7	287	8
Conserved as:						
Hay	251	8	—	—	251	7
Silage	577	19	—	—	577	15
	3106	100	622	100	3728	100

161.4 acres. The acreage is based on the Ordnance Survey acreages of the fields and is, therefore, probably rather higher than the acreage actually available, which was about 150. Hence the output of starch equivalent per acre was $\frac{3515}{150}$ = 23·4 cwt. This can be compared with the national figures on page 124 and it will be seen that our figures are appreciably better as already stated. This greater production can be accounted for by efficient fertilising, controlled grazing and better utilisation all round. Moreover, all ploughable fields are in fact ploughed and put through a rotation to incorporate a four-year grass and clover ley. These leys are generally accepted to be much more productive than permanent grassland. The figure obtained for the College Farm is by no means the best that can be secured for grassland; many examples could be quoted where, due to a more fertile soil, better rainfall distribution or the use of irrigation in dry periods, yields of 35 to 40 cwt. per acre of utilised starch equivalent have been recorded. High fertility and an adequate well-distributed water supply, when allied to the right species of grasses and first class management, can produce quite spectacular results. Anyone who wishes to pursue this intriguing problem further and perhaps record the output of grass on a specific farm should read Baker, H. K. *et. al. The Journal of the British Grassland Society* (1964), volume 19, number 1, pages 139 to 168.

CHAPTER 16

THE ECONOMICS OF GRASSLAND FARMING

The value of grassland to the nation depends upon its productivity in terms of food for human consumption when compared with the other possible uses to which the same land could be put. Is it more desirable in the interests of the nation as a whole that a certain acreage of land grows grass or would it be better under wheat or potatoes or vegetables? That, in simple terms, is the vital question. Unfortunately, however, as we have seen, the productivity of grassland is not easily measured with the precision of those crops which are final products for sale, such as grain or roots. These are weighed and sold off the farm at a given price and the productivity of the land is determined by simple arithmetic.

Grass is not a finished product, with a readily ascertained market price, but simply a raw material which must be processed into animal products before it is of direct use to man. To complicate the issue still further, grass is quite often only one of the constituents in the diet of farm animals and it is very difficult in practice to separate the influence of each constituent on the growth and productivity of the animals. What is more, the animals themselves are individuals and react differently to varying diets. Some are inherently "good doers," some are extremely fastidious in what they eat, others have voracious appetites and are quite indifferent to quality, provided the food is supplied in adequate quantity. Obviously this individuality complicates still further the problem of measuring the value of grass.

Despite these difficulties, however, and the frequent necessity to qualify the results obtained, many calculations have been made both of the national output of grassland and of the output on selected farms and experimental plots.

The calculation of the national output is a matter of importance and interest for two reasons. First, the fact that two out of every three

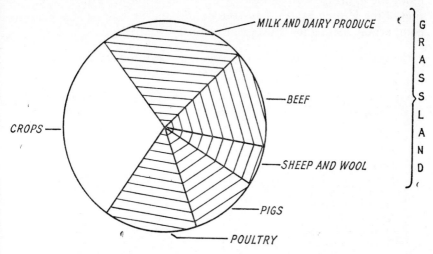

FIG. 4. DISTRIBUTION OF BRITISH AGRICULTURAL OUTPUT

acres of the farmed land of this country are under grass makes it necessary that we should know whether this land, which is fixed in supply and our most secure and lasting asset should an emergency arise, is used most efficiently, not merely in the interest of farmers as producers but of the citizens of the nation as consumers. Secondly, British agriculture, as shown in Fig. 4, is overwhelmingly concerned with livestock production. Of this, that portion derived from the predominantly grazing animals, cattle and sheep, forms the greater part. Moreover, important as grassland production is to-day, it must become even more important in the future, for, as societies develop and standards of living increase, dietary habits change. Amongst poorer communities emphasis falls upon the cheaper energy-giving foods such as the cereals, beans, peas, and roots, whereas in the wealthier communities the more expensive and more palatable high-quality vegetables and fruit dominate the diet, together with larger quantities of meat and livestock products. A further potent factor in developing the demand for meat, milk, and dairy produce is the raising of the standard of education throughout the country and the general dissemination and acquisition of more knowledge of the nutritional and protective qualities of these foods. In some countries the consumption of meat and livestock products is hindered by custom and religion but where no such impediment exists, the amounts of these products consumed per head are good indicators of the level of economic and social development. The following figures, issued in 1960 by the Food and Agriculture Organisation of the United States, show the position of the United Kingdom in comparison with some European countries and the U.S.A.

TABLE 16. MEAT AND MILK SUPPLIES AVAILABLE FOR HUMAN CONSUMPTION IN CERTAIN COUNTRIES—1958-9

Country	Meat	*Milk and Milk Products
	lb. per head per annum	
Denmark	155	510
France	.149	414
Holland	94	550
Italy	53	244
Sweden	114	550
United Kingdom	149	450
United States	198	580
Western Germany	114	440

* Milk and milk products estimated in terms of liquid milk

On the legitimate assumption that the pattern of our diet will tend towards that of the U.S.A. the more closely we achieve their degree of economic wealth, then the conclusion to be reached is that more meat will be needed. Inevitably this means that a very much greater role must be played by grass in the future.

To return to the question of the existing productivity of grass, what is the situation? Fig. 4 shows that nearly three-quarters of the output of British agriculture consists of livestock products. Of the total just under half is accounted for by grass-eating animals. As previously stated, these animals also eat varying proportions of other foods and the problem becomes one of isolating the contribution made by grass alone. Many attempts to do this have been made as we discussed in chapter 15, and these have usually been on the basis of calculating the theoretical food requirements of the animals and the level of outputs achieved, and assuming that this represents their total consumption. Foods, other than grass, can be measured more accurately (e.g. the tonnage of cereals or root crops fed); their nutritional value is then calculated, deducted from the total requirements, and the remainder is assumed to be the contribution made by grass. This type of calculation has one major drawback, namely that any errors made in calculating the food needs of the animals, or in calculating the food value of the fodder and cereals fed, are reflected in the estimate for grass, which is simply a difference figure. Nevertheless the calculation provides some

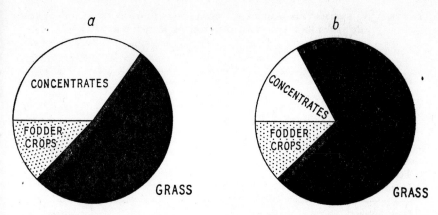

FIG. 5 THE RELATIVE IMPORTANCE OF DIFFERENT SOURCES OF FEED
FOR CATTLE AND SHEEP

Measured "a" by cost, "b" by nutrients supplied

indication of the general level of grassland productivity and its contribution to the production of human food. Thus it has been estimated
that the grass-eating animal population of the United Kingdom needs
annually a total slightly in excess of $20\frac{1}{2}$ million tons of starch
equivalent and that of this figure, feeds other than grass provide just
about $5\frac{3}{4}$ million tons, leaving a residue provided by grass amounting
to $14\frac{3}{4}$ million tons. Thus grass provides 72 per cent of the total food
intake (see Fig. 5b). What is the value of this? It could be valued in
terms of the most commonly used alternative, namely imported feed,
and this would yield an estimated value, on the farm, of about £700m.
It would, however, be quite impracticable to replace all our grassland
by imported feed. A more realistic assessment of its worth to the nation
would be to indicate that, of the total U.K. output of £1,040m.
worth of livestock products at farm gate prices, £460m. may be
attributed to grass.

The contribution of grass to the earning power of farmers and to
the supplies of high-quality home foods is, therefore, large. Is it,
however, as large as is desirable, or as large as it could be?

It is undeniable that grass and grass products are the cheapest form
of foods for herbivorous animals. The Grassland Utilisation Committee quoted the figures shown in the following table for 1956-7, and
subsequent farming developments have not invalidated the comparison
between one crop and another.

TABLE 17. ESTIMATED AVERAGE COSTS OF PRODUCTION OF STARCH
EQUIVALENT FOR VARIOUS CROPS AND DAIRY CAKE

	cost per ton of *starch equivalent* £
Grazing	12·6
Kale-grazed	17·6
Barley	19·6
Hay in stack	21·8
Grass silage	23·0
Oats	25·8
Arable silage	32·0
Turnips and swedes	34·6
Dried grass	39·8
Dairy cake	46·2

The cost advantage in favour of grass is even more strikingly demonstrated by the diagrams on page 129 which show the constituents of the national feed bill in terms of nutrient provided by cost on the one hand, or quantity of nutrient on the other. Grass provides three-quarters of the nutrients, but only accounts for one-half the feed cost. It is clear, therefore, that any replacement of concentrates and other fodder by grass reduces the costs of livestock production.

All the evidence suggests that the contribution of grass could be greater. In the first place, the average yield of starch equivalent per acre in this country is substantially lower than in many other countries enjoying conditions no more favourable than ours. The result of an O.E.E.C. survey published in 1954 demonstrated that grassland production in the United Kingdom was only a fraction of the productivity of some of our European competitors. The relative position of the nine countries included in the survey is shown in the table below:

TABLE 18. INDICES OF GRASSLAND PRODUCTIVITY

	U.K.=100
Netherlands	158
Denmark	132
Belgium	120
Norway	112
West Germany	108
United Kingdom	100
Austria	87
Ireland	83
France	67

PLATE 13. Modern methods. *Above*, harvesting with a combine and pick-up baler for straw. *Below*, zero-grazing. The grass is mown and brought to the cattle

PLATE 14. Types of pasture. *Above*, rough moorland grazing with hardy Galloway cattle. *Below*, spring-time in Northamptonshire, near Church Stowe

The significance of these figures is that if the United Kingdom achieved the Dutch level of grassland productivity the additional S.E. produced would be equivalent to roughly one and a half times that now imported from abroad in the form of concentrates. Even though the substitution of all imported feed by grass and grass products—hay, silage and dried grass—may not be practicable for husbandry reasons, there is substantial scope for saving. This is further emphasised by the fact that individual farmers are known to achieve grassland yields two or three times as high as the average.

The aggregate figures demonstrate clearly that the grass crop is the broad foundation upon which the greater part of the nation's large and growing livestock industry is built. Equally important, they indicate that there is substantial scope for further exploitation—but it remains to demonstrate how this can put money in the farmer's pocket.

There is a great deal of evidence on the profit-making possibilities of grass, some of it related to results obtained at experimental stations and some to results on ordinary commercial farms. It is not intended to review the evidence exhaustively but merely to present a few examples drawn from ordinary farm experience, relating both to meat and milk production.

The profit-making potential of grass in meat production is well-illustrated both for beef and sheep in the analysis of the results of groups of farms in the west country. Both the cattle and sheep-producing farms have been divided into three groups according to the level of profitability per acre which they achieved, and their feeding practices have been examined. Table 19 shows the results for a group of farms producing beef by the single suckling method, whereby each cow suckles her own calf.

The figures show clearly that the above average farms, by efficient grassland management, achieved heavy rates of stocking per acre, reduced their dependence upon other more expensive foods, particularly those bought in, and in consequence enjoyed double the average level of profits and over three times the profit of the below average group. This last group made least intensive use of grass, but grew and bought in larger quantities of food to make good the deficiency. The conclusion of this analysis is that intensive stocking of well-managed grassland is the way to higher profits from beef production.

Similar results were found by Beynon when the records of sheep-producing farms were analysed (table 20).

G.G.   K

TABLE 19. FEEDING PRACTICES, LIVEWEIGHT INCREASES, AND PROFIT
PER ACRE ON BEEF-PRODUCING FARMS AT DIFFERENT LEVELS OF PROFIT

	farms with profits		
	below average	*average*	*above average*
		feed acres per breeding cow	
home grown feed			
Grazing	3·71	3·43	2·91
Conserved grass	0·95	0·89	0·79
Total grassland	4·66	4·32	3·70
Other home grown foods	0·98	0·92	0·82
Total home grown	5·64	5·24	4·52
bought in feed			
Equivalent in acres	0·14	0·10	0·01
Total feed acres	5·78	5·34	4·53
		per feed acre	
Liveweight increase lb.	165	188	230
Total output (£)	14·1	15·7	18·3
Profit (£)	2·0	3·5	6·7

Once more, the farms with the highest profits producing the largest
quantities of meat and wool make the most intensive use of grass.
Although the above average farms have an output of nearly 200 lb.
of mutton and lamb per acre, under more closely controlled conditions
outputs of 400 to 500 lb. per acre have been achieved. It seems, therefore, that even above-average farms still have scope for improvement.

In the case of that most important branch of livestock husbandry,
milk production, the situation is a little more complicated. The modern
dairy cow, as a result of countless generations of highly selective
breeding, is often capable of yields of milk perhaps five or six times
that necessary simply to suckle her young. The aim is not to obtain
maximum growth, but to provide the animal with food of such quality
and in such quantity as to make this high production of milk possible
and at the same time maintain the animal in good health. Basically,
the problem stems from the fact that a dairy cow's appetite and ability
to consume food have not increased proportionately to her milk-
producing capacity. For this reason the high-yielding cow requires
food of high nutritive value in relation to its bulk. Thus by long-
established custom, the cow is fed substantial quantities of cereals

TABLE 20. FEEDING PRACTICES, LIVEWEIGHT INCREASES, AND PROFIT
PER ACRE ON MUTTON-PRODUCING FARMS AT DIFFERENT LEVELS OF PROFIT

	farms with profits		
	below average	*average*	*above average*
		feed acres per breeding ewe	
home grown feed			
Grazing	0·59	0·56	0·53
Conserved grass	—	—	—
Total grassland	0·59	0·56	0·53
Other home grown foods	0·04	0·06	0·07
Total	0·63	0·62	0·60
bought in feed			
Equivalent in acres	0·01	0·01	—
Total feed acres	0·64	0·63	0·60
		per feed acre	
Breeding ewes	1·56	1·59	1·67
Liveweight increase lb.	150	169	197
Wool (lb.)	20	22	26
Total output (£)	14·9	16·2	18·3
Profit (£)	8·4	9·4	10·8

together with the by-products of the seed-oil extraction processes.
These latter foods are high in energy and protein and with the cereals
are generally bracketed together under the name of "concentrates."
The practice of feeding concentrates to dairy cows was greatly
facilitated by the pre-war availability of very cheap imported supplies
of feeding cereals and oil seed cake. The practice still persists but the
economics of the situation have changed drastically. Whereas the
price the farmer receives for his milk has increased about four-fold
since 1939, the price of dairy cake has increased about five- to six-fold.
With the current tendency to produce milk in excess of requirements,
it seems reasonably certain that the milk price received by the farmer
is not likely to improve and may even decrease in the coming years.
The effect of this must be for the milk/feed price ratio to become more
unfavourable. In these circumstances, the more progressive farmers
have explored the possibility of reducing their dependence upon
expensive concentrates and have set about developing systems of
cheaper milk production. In this way profits and living standards

can be maintained. The fuller exploitation of grass has been the spear-head of the attack; many successes have been achieved and some data are available to indicate the possibilities.

The Report of the National Investigation into Milk Production, 1955-7, analysed the profitability of milk production. Farms were grouped according to their level of production of nutrients per acre secured from grass, silage and kale, grass being of predominant importance. This analysis clearly showed that farmers who obtained most cow food from their land also secured the highest rate of profit. The figures are shown in table 21 below:

TABLE 21. STARCH EQUIVALENT PRODUCTION PER ACRE OF GRASS-LAND, ARABLE SILAGE AND KALE

	Low (10·4 cwt.)	Medium (13·8 cwt.)	High (17·9 cwt.)
Number of farms	104	165	97
Profit per acre used for dairy cows:	£	£	£
1955-6	8·1	11·4	13·0
1956-7	6·6	10·7	12·8

Although it is likely that the higher profits were associated with factors other than grassland utilisation, such as better livestock husbandry generally and higher yields of both crops and milk, it is evident that there is close correlation between the efficient use of home-grown foods—especially grass—and high profits. An analysis of summer milk production costs and returns on a number of eastern counties farms over a five-year period, shows similar conclusions, but even more forcibly (table 22).

This table contains many lessons. Firstly, farmers making most use of grass spend most money per acre on producing it, but the cost per unit of nutrient is less. In other words, the increase in output within this range of grassland yields is more than proportionate to the increase in cost. Secondly, those farmers with the highest food production have more to feed and are able to substitute cheap food in the form of grass for the more expensive other foods—largely concentrates. Thirdly, the more productive the grass the greater the number of cows per acre which can be carried. Thus maximum profits are secured from the fixed factor in farming, namely land. The overall result on these farms is that the margin over feed costs per cow during the summer increases from £17 19s. od. for those farms making least

TABLE 22. THE INFLUENCE OF GRAZING PRODUCTIVITY ON THE COSTS AND RETURNS OF SUMMER MILK PRODUCTION

Yield Group (cwt. starch equivalent per acre of grazing)	Up to 7·5	7·5- 10·0	10·0- 12·5	12·5- 15·0	15·0 & over
Average yield of starch equivalent per acre (cwt.)	5·76	8·66	11·17	13·61	18·63
Quantity of milk provided by an acre of grazing (gallons)	113	162	216	258	360
1. COST					
Per acre of grazing	£3 8s	£4 2s	£4 14s	£5 2s	£5 10s
Per cwt. of starch equivalent	11s 10d	9s 6d	8s 5d	7s 6d	5s 11d
Per gallon of milk	7·22d	6·07d	5·22d	4·74d	3·67d
2. FEED SUBSTITUTION					
Yield per cow in summer (gallons)	390	367	379	374	389
Acres grazed per cow	1·54	1·32	1·15	0·95	0·76
Gallons per cow in summer from:					
Grazing	174	214	248	245	274
Other foods	216	153	131	129	115
Cost per cow in summer of:	£ s	£ s	£ s	£ s	£ s
Grazing	5 5	5 8	5 8	4 17	4 4
Other foods	20 14	14 13	12 11	12 7	11 —
TOTAL COST	25 19	20 1	17 19	17 4	15 4
3. MARGIN PER ACRE OF GRAZING	£ s	£ s	£ s	£ s	£ s
Receipts per cow in summer	43 18	41 6	42 13	42 2	43 15
Receipts per acre	28 10	31 6	37 2	44 6	57 11
Grazing and other food costs per acre	16 17	15 4	15 12	18 2	20 —
Margin per acre	11 13	16 2	21 10	26 4	37 11

use of grass to £28 11s. od. per cow on farms where the most use of grass is made. Taking into account, however, the larger number of cows carried on any given area by the farmer maximising the use of his grass, the margin per acre of land increases from £11 13s. od., on the one hand, to no less a sum than £37 11s. od. on the other: a margin over three times as great.

In the face of these striking results, it is hard to understand why farmers do not make more use of Nature's greatest gift—good grass.

Time and again in this book we have seen that a high degree of skill is necessary to ensure that the grass plant is amply nourished, and utilised, without waste, at the peak of its productive life. Either this skill is not available, or the majority of farmers find it less exacting—even though less profitable—to purchase their stock food in bags from a merchant.

CHAPTER 17

OTHER IMPORTANT ECONOMIC GRASSES

The species generally considered by the layman as "grass" are grown for their vegetative parts, whether for feeding to livestock or merely for man's pleasure: the cereals, also members of the grass family, are cultivated for their grain. So far as we know, all the important civilisations of the world have relied on one or more of the cereals as the staple food for the human population.

Originally, the cereals were derived from wild grasses and by selection and various breeding methods have reached their present highly advanced state of cultivation. The "wild progenitors" of some of the cereals still exist and in many cases it is possible to trace with reasonable certainty the botanical history of our present-day crops.

As the domestication of livestock progressed, so the cereals were used as animal fodder to supplement the available grass, while the straw provided excellent bedding and formed an ideal medium for the production of farm-yard manure, which, until about thirty years ago, was the principal means of maintaining soil fertility. The ever-increasing population of the world has meant a constant emphasis on the need for grain-producing crops and so the acreage under cereals has been rising steadily. By constantly improved methods of cultivation the yield of grain per acre has increased, and the granaries of the world have been supplied.

It is not difficult to appreciate why the cereals have become so universally cultivated. They are adaptable to a wide range of soil and climatic conditions and lend themselves admirably to straightforward, routine cultivation. The actual growing of the crop does not present any great difficulty as it does with some crops with very specialised requirements. Grain stores well in large quantities and supplies can be carried over from one season to another. Equally important, grain is easily transported over vast distances by land or sea.

Cereals are also comparatively easy to breed. All the common cereals, other than rye, are self-pollinating—although occasional cross-pollination may occur—and single-plant selections can, therefore, be used as the basis for all breeding work. Selection of the progeny from single plants enables a high degree of uniformity to be obtained and when all the possibilities of selection are exhausted new types can be created by carefully planned hybridisation, followed by equally careful selection.

All the important cereals are annuals and thus can be sown in the spring and harvested in the same growing season. Some varieties of wheat, barley, oats, and rye may be sown in the autumn and are sufficiently hardy to withstand the winter; they are then harvested the following summer, when they usually ripen slightly earlier than varieties which are sown in the spring. From the farmer's point of view autumn sowing has many advantages for it spreads both seed time and harvest over many more weeks than would be possible if all varieties had to be sown in the spring. In this way, peak periods of labour demand are avoided.

Wheat is grown primarily for human consumption and for milling into flour, while barley may be grown for the maltster or brewer. On soils which are too rich for the malting varieties, feeding barleys, giving a higher yield of lower quality grain, are an excellent alternative, and, indeed, constitute by far the greater proportion of barley grown to-day. Oats on the other hand, are grown almost entirely for feeding to farm livestock. Oat straw has considerable value as a fodder and the crop can be cut and harvested quite satisfactorily in an unripe condition. The value of this crop largely depends on the fact that it enables cereal growing to be extended to those parts where, due to the lack of sunshine or warmth, wheat and barley would fail to ripen and where, owing to high rainfall, grain growing would be most hazardous.

Wheat was grown in this country in the New Stone Age and, with successive invasions, new types were introduced. But in early historical times barley, and later rye and oats, were also grown as bread corn. It is only in the last hundred years that wheat has become the major source of bread flour in this country; so much so that we are no longer able to supply our needs from home-grown grain and are now one of the largest importers in the world. Europe, North America, and the U.S.S.R. produce the great bulk of the world's crop.

The popularity of wheat for bread-making is due to the particular characteristics of its protein (gluten), which allow the baker to produce the light-textured, spongy loaf which modern tastes demand. Some of the qualities which go to make up a good bread wheat are inherited, others are dependent on the growing, harvesting, threshing, and storing conditions to which the wheat is subjected. Although bread wheats can be grown in this country, the variable climate and the large numbers of farmers involved give rise to a good deal of variability and millers can handle foreign wheat, which is much more uniform and can be secured in large consignments, more economically. Moreover, more loaves can be produced from a given amount of flour from imported grain than from home-grown wheat, which is also more expensive to buy. Our own wheat is now grown for manufacture into animal feedstuffs and for making biscuit flours. So farmers concentrate on securing the highest yield of grain per acre and have not to consider the baking quality of any particular variety grown.

The botanical classification of the wheats is exceedingly complex, and I cannot discuss it here; for an excellent modern treatment see Bowden (1959). The most important wheat is *Triticum* × *æstivum*. Many thousands of different varieties are in existence, and plant breeders are constantly seeking new and improved types, but the range of varieties actually used is contracting. For example, in this country at the present time 60 per cent of the acreage sown is confined to the variety Cappelle Desprez. There are indications, however, that in a few years' time one or two of the newer varieties which can beat it in yield and compare favourably with it in other characteristics will replace it.

In this country, wheat is mainly sown in the autumn from September to December, with October as the best time. Spring varieties will be sown from February to April, with March as the ideal month for most types.

Barley (*Hordeum sativum*) was used for making bread and fermented drinks in the most ancient civilisations of the Old World. Gradually, however, wheat with its superior bread-making qualities replaced barley in this field and barley became a crop grown primarily for brewing and, more latterly, for feeding to livestock. The distribution of this crop is as wide in temperate regions as that of wheat, but it has the added advantage that it can often be grown where wheat can not. The hardiest types of barley are cultivated at high altitudes in many mountainous regions of the world and are grown as far north as the Arctic Circle.

The bulk of the crop is sown in spring and most of the home-produced grain is used by maltsters and brewers, although some brewing barley is imported. Sixty per cent of the malting barley grown to-day is the variety Proctor, bred at the Plant Breeding Institute,

Cambridge. Another product from Cambridge, Maris Badger, which became available in 1963, is mildew resistant as well as being stiffer in the straw than Proctor. The finest samples of malting barley are grown in the south-east of England and in certain coastal areas in Devon, Somerset, and south-east Scotland. Feeding barleys may be sown in the autumn or spring and the emphasis in their case is on yield per acre. The genus *Hordeum*, to which the cultivated barleys belong, also includes a number of grasses growing wild in Britain. For a discussion of the relationship between wild and cultivated barleys see Bowden (1959).

For brewing purposes, the grain must have special qualities. In cross section the grain must be white and starchy, while the skin should be finely-wrinkled, indicating the right degree of ripeness. It must have a clear, pale-yellow colour, showing that the weather at harvesting time was favourable. The nitrogen content of the grain must be low. The grain must be undamaged by the process of threshing, because damaged grains mould on the malting floor instead of germinating and give rise to taints in the beer. In the malting process the grain is soaked and allowed to germinate for just over a week. Chemical changes take place within the grain and there is considerable root development. The germination is then stopped by kiln-drying, and the shrivelled roots are removed by sieving. The residue is the malt, which is then incubated with water, and the enzyme diastase which is present breaks down the starch to maltose. The extract from this process is fermented with yeast to produce alcohol.

The oldest records show oats as a weed in other crops and these weed oats formed the progenitors of our modern varieties. Oats are much more accommodating than wheat or barley, and this is the cereal cultivated under the widest range of conditions in the British Isles. It is said that wherever a plough can turn a furrow a crop of oats can be secured. There is a wide selection of varieties which may be sown in the autumn or the spring and, in addition to the production of grain for feeding, the crop is often grown for cutting green, either alone or in association with beans, peas, or vetches. The mixed crop can be carried through to harvest and threshed for mixed grain if desired. Oats belong to the genus *Avena*, which has also a number of species growing wild in Britain, including the two common weeds, *A. fatua* and *A. ludoviciana*. The most important cultivated varieties belong to the species *A. sativa*, but in the upland and hilly districts of Wales, Scotland, and the Shetlands some *A. strigosa* forms, which are better suited to poor soils and wetter conditions, are still grown. A third oat species—*A. byzantina*—is not grown in this country but has been used for hybridising.

Rye (*Secale cereale*) was first cultivated some two thousand years ago, probably in Asia Minor, whence it has spread throughout the temperate zone. It has the merit that it can be grown under conditions quite unsuitable for the other cereals, wheat demanding sunshine and barley failing on land lacking lime; oats are rather less discriminating, but rye can withstand soil acidity, poor hungry land and dry light soils, where wheat, barley or oats would be failures.

These characteristics, together with the fact that it can be used for making rye bread, which is preferred by some peoples, mean that it shares first place with wheat in the U.S.S.R., Poland, Germany, Scandinavia, and the central European states. In this country, it is used chiefly as a green forage crop for feeding to livestock, apart from the small acreage grown for rye crispbread. The straw is slender, long and wiry, and valuable for thatching, for making bottle containers, and for packing, on account of its hardness. Winter and spring varieties are available, but owing to frequent cross-pollination, varieties are few and by no means as uniform as in other cereals. Rye has always been of value to us in war time because it can be grown successfully on poor, ploughed-up grassland which, under normal circumstances, is not worth cultivating. Rye flour has been used for mixing with wheaten flour for bread-making and for stock feed.

Rice (*Oryza sativa*) is as important as wheat as a food crop; it has been estimated that half the world's population subsists wholly or partly on rice. The world crop is estimated at over 150 million tons annually.

The original home of rice is uncertain. For a long time it was believed that its cultivation began in China. There are fields in China, for instance, where it is thought to have been grown continuously for at least four thousand years. In 2,700 B.C., the Emperor Shên-nung, the Father of Agriculture and Medicine, ordained that the season of rice sowing would be opened ceremonially by himself at the vernal equinox, when he would sow the first and best seeds of rice. Afterwards, four other kinds would be sown by princes of his family. Many present-day varieties of rice may have originated, however, from the wild forms of rice species in India called by the natives, *Newarre*, or *Nivara* as recorded by Roxburgh in "Flora Indica." Hector mentions wild forms in India under the name of *Oryza sativa* var. *spontanea*. From India, it may have spread through China, Japan, Siam and thence to the islands of the Far East. It is also possible that tropical Africa was its fatherland, whence it must have been carried to Asia very early indeed. It reached Europe via the Arabs, who introduced it into Spain.

The introduction of rice to North America is attributed to Sir William Buckley who from 1647 tried for several years to grow it in Virginia but with little success. Some fifty years later, a vessel of the East India Company bound for Liverpool from Madagascar was blown off course and put into Charleston, South Carolina. It is recorded that a certain trader named Thomas Smith boarded the ship and was given a present of a bag of the rough (unhulled) rice known as "paddy." Smith planted the rice on some swampy ground where it grew very successfully and produced a crop reputed to be large enough to feed the entire colony. By 1707, rice growing was so well established in South Carolina that seventeen ships, completely laden with the grain, sailed for foreign ports. To-day, some of the finest rice in the world comes from Arkansas, California, Louisiana, and Texas.

The plant is an annual with long, smooth, narrow leaves and stems from two to five feet long. The fact that there are about two thousand distinct varieties, sufficient to meet all needs of soil type, range of climate and systems of cultivation, testifies to the great age of rice as a cereal crop. It thrives in tropical and sub-tropical climates where fresh water is in abundant supply. On flat ground it is often grown under irrigation, provided the soil has sufficient body to retain the water, for the plants must be submerged in from four to eight inches. Static water means that the area is liable to become malarial and this has undoubtedly restricted its cultivation in southern Europe.

In China and the Far East, the crop is still cultivated by hand. The seed rice is broadcast in a specially prepared bed which is flooded as soon as the plants reach a height of three inches. When they have grown to six inches, the bed is drained and the seedlings are lifted and carried to the swampy rice fields, where they are planted out by hand. The rice fields are kept flooded until the plants are some fifteen inches high when they are drained, the crop is weeded and hoed by hand, and then once more the field is flooded until the crop is ready for harvesting. In America, normal mechanised cultivations are carried out to prepare the seed bed and the seed is drilled direct as with other grain crops. The water for irrigation is obtained from streams or pumped from wells and is then distributed to the rice fields through a system of canals. In many areas, and particularly in California, the seed is sown from aeroplanes direct on to the flooded fields. Water-seeded rice usually ripens more uniformly, and better control of grass and weeds is possible, than when the crop is sown in the normal fashion.

The spikelets with their flowers are produced on a branched head which bends down from an erect position as the plant develops. When the grains in the upper spikelets are on the point of ripeness the land is drained, and about two weeks later the crop will be fit for harvesting.

Rice is harvested by means of a combine or binder which may be self-propelled or hitched to a tractor. As with wheat, if the crop is cut with a binder and tied into sheaves these must first dry out in the stook before they can be threshed. When a combine is used the grain must be dried artificially before it can be processed.

The grain, like barley and oats, but unlike wheat, retains the husk when it leaves the threshing machine and is known as rough or "paddy" rice. This is used for seed or for feeding to livestock. For human consumption it must first be milled. When just the husk is removed, brown rice is obtained, which, because it retains minerals, protein and vitamins, is a more valuable foodstuff than polished rice but because of its unattractive colour is less popular. Hence further milling (polishing) is carried out, which removes the bran, the germ and the aleurone layer.

When stripped of its outer skins by machinery, this foodstuff, the staple diet of millions, loses nearly all the oil, a good deal of protein and almost all the minerals and vitamins, leaving it composed of about 90 to 94 per cent starch. Where rice constitutes the major item in the diet these deficiencies give rise to a multiple neuritis, a disease called beri-beri (weakness), which was not diagnosed until about 1890. To-day, it is possible for rice to be milled to preserve the bran layers and germ, or vitamin B. can be added to the polished rice, so that the disease no longer takes its toll of human life. Much the same is true of wheat. Modern milling and treatments to produce a pure white loaf of spongy texture remove the bran and germ, and a diet consisting of bread made from this flour would lead to malnutrition. Fortunately, our diet in the West is generally too varied for this to happen and, in any event, both bran and wheat germ are on sale as special foods for those who need their particular qualities.

Rice in modern times is used in a wide variety of ways and forms both in the East and the West. Glue, starch, sugar and rice wines are made from the grain. In China and Japan, a very fine type of paper is produced from the straw of the rice plant, which is also used for feeding and bedding livestock, while in other eastern countries it is used for thatching roofs and making ropes, sandals and other articles more usually made from cereal straws in the West.

The origin of maize (*Zea mays*), or Indian corn, has been studied by

Mangelsdorf and others, and there seems little doubt that it was developed from a wild progenitor in Central America at least four or five thousand years ago. Primitive types of maize have been found preserved in a cave in New Mexico, where they were probably introduced from Mexico. During the development of the many present-day varieties hybridisation has certainly taken place with the allied grass teosinte (*Euchlæna mexicana*) which itself may be a hybrid between maize and another grass, *Tripsacum dactyloides*.

Lyte in his *Nievve Herball* of 1578, says "This corne is a marvellous strange plante, nothing resembling any other kinde of grayne," and its mode of reproduction perplexed European botanists for a long time when it was first introduced from America, "for it bringethe foorth his seeds cleane contrarie from the place where as the flowers growe." The plant is an annual, with a stout solid stem and large fleshy, broad-bladed leaves, usually producing only one shoot. Unlike most other grasses, however, the terminal panicle, which is called the "tassel," a very apt description, bears only male flowers. These open and pollen is shed on to the female flowers borne on separate inflorescences called "cobs," which are produced in the axils of some of the middle leaves of the main stem. These cobs have a short, stout stem from the lower part of which closely-packed imbricating and almost bladeless leaves emerge which enclose the upper fertile part of the inflorescence and form the husk. Each female flower bears a single thread-like style, long enough to emerge above the husks as the dainty pink or orchid-coloured "silks" which are characteristic of the plant. When it has been pollinated, each flower develops to form a single grain of corn on the developing cob. The silks then wither, the husk leaves become dry and papery, and the grain passes from the "milk" stage, when each grain is filled with a whitish liquid, to one where the grains are hard and ready for harvest. These grains are still held tightly-packed on the axis of the cob. Thus there can be no normal means of dispersal for the seed, a fact which caused much confusion in the minds of early botanists when the plant was first discovered.

Many wonderful Indian legends tell of miraculous beginnings for the crop. Its cultivation spread rapidly, for the Indian was skilled in the art of plant breeding and developed many varieties to meet his needs. To-day, it is America's most important crop and the only grain referred to there as corn. Its uses are many; meal and flour, alcoholic drinks and sweet syrups. It is eaten as a green vegetable. Its stalks are even used for walls, fences and roofs as can be seen in whole villages in Guatemala.

As far as Europe is concerned, the discovery of maize seems to date from 5th November, 1492, when sailors landed by Columbus to explore the interior of Cuba brought back word of this grain which, they said, had a good taste and a variety of uses. When the Spaniards arrived in Peru, they found vast stores of grain of different types and colours. To-day, the cultivation of the crop is widespread and, in many countries where the climate does not allow the grain to ripen, maize is grown for green fodder or silage.

From the beginning of this century, we in this country have used the variety White Horse Tooth for silage making. This variety is really a late, high-yielding variety grown for grain in the southern States of the U.S.A. but is grown in Britain for its vegetative growth. The grain yield over here is negligible but the leafage very abundant. In all districts where summer drought is liable to restrict the growth of grass, maize provides an invaluable insurance crop in the shape of succulent leaves and stems, which when fed to dairy cows, help to maintain the output of milk under trying conditions. Unfortunately the crop is very susceptible to frost and the majority of maize varieties will not germinate satisfactorily when the soil temperature falls below 50° F. Its cultivation must be restricted to the warmer regions of England, although in a favourable season good crops have been secured as far north as Yorkshire. New hybrid varieties are constantly being introduced from the U.S.A. and the Netherlands, where in a very favourable season the grain may even ripen. The great advantage of these varieties is that they reach a state of near-maturity, in contrast to the old variety White Horse Tooth. Consequently they have a higher dry matter content and produce a more valuable type of silage. The use of maize for silage making in this country is, therefore, developing quite rapidly and there is no doubt that if plant breeders could secure a variety which would ripen grain regularly under English climatic conditions, it would probably oust barley as the most common cereal grown for stock feeding. For this purpose, it would have the advantage of giving higher yields of grain per acre and, being grown in rows, could replace the fodder root crop as the cleaning crop of the rotation. The United States grows about half the world's crop, some $83\frac{1}{4}$ million acres being grown each year, and the bulk of this is used for livestock feeding. Deep, rich, free-working loam soils are ideal for maize which has a growing season varying from two to seven months according to variety. The whole process of cultivation from sowing the seed to harvesting the grain can be mechanised.

A cane-like grass which resembles the tall varieties of maize is sorghum (*Sorghum vulgare*), although the stem is more slender and the plant does not produce separate male and female inflorescences. The sorghums are of African origin and may be grown for stock food, forage or syrup, while the stiff open panicles of some varieties are used, after seeding, for making brooms. The crop is well suited to primitive agriculture, needing less care and attention than other cereals. The seed is smaller than wheat and may be white, red, yellow, or brown in colour, while the seeds are rounded, flattened or ellipsoid. Since the crop is very resistant to heat and drought it is well adapted to arid regions and is extremely valuable under such difficult conditions. The grain is comparable in feeding value to maize and for human consumption it is ground into a meal and made into porridge or cakes.

Also amongst the grain crops of importance in East Asia is millet, a name used for quite a number of distinct grasses. Common millet (*Panicum miliaceum*) has been cultivated since prehistoric times in Egypt, Asia, and southern Europe. Foxtail millet (*Setaria italica*), with a denser panicle than common millet, is also grown as a grain crop, particularly in Asia. However, as methods of cultivation improve with the development of these areas, millet is tending to be replaced by the larger-grained and higher-yielding cereals. In North America it is used mainly for forage.

One grass, the giant perennial sugar cane (*Saccharum officinarum* and allied species) has been prized for its sweet juice from ancient times. It is one of the few perennial grasses whose vegetative parts are used for human food and, in contrast to other grasses, is selected for sterility. This grass is now grown in all tropical and sub-tropical countries and some two thirds of the world's annual sugar production of around fifty million tons is produced from it. Moist, rich soil, preferably near to the sea, suits it best.

As with so many cultivated grasses the origin of *S. officinarum* is a matter of speculation but the consensus of opinion seems to indicate New Guinea for some forms and India for others, while hybridisation with the wild *S. spontaneum* has probably played a part in its development. From India the cane spread east and west. In all probability the Phœnicians brought it as an eastern curiosity to Europe about 1500 B.C. A writer in A.D. 1108 recorded that the "Crusaders found sweet-honeyed reeds in great quantity in the meadows about Tripoli." The Saracens are reputed to have originated sugar cultivation in Sicily, Rhodes and Cyprus, while the Moors introduced the crop to Africa and Spain. The Portuguese carried it to Madeira and later the

PLATE 15. Pampas grass, a decorative species in gardens

PLATE 16. Grass for leisure. Cricket at Brockham, golf at Tyrrells Wood (both in Surrey)

Spaniards to the Canary Islands, but it was not until the seventeenth century that the Dutch and English commenced cultivation in the West Indies. The vogue for tea and coffee is said to have given the industry the necessary impetus for such immense production.

The grass grows to around fifteen feet in height and has stout, solid stems from which the sugar is extracted by crushing. The plant is normally propagated vegetatively. The stems or canes vary in diameter from half an inch to three inches, with the nodes from four to six inches apart, terminating in a great panicle of flowers, although the crop is cut before flowering occurs. The canes, which are yellowish green at first, vary in colour as ripening progresses according to variety; there are purple, red, yellow, striped and blotched canes, and some are almost black.

The leaf blades spring from a sheath about a foot long which completely surrounds the stalk just above a node. The blades are three to four feet long and two to three inches wide at the base tapering to a point with serrated edges. At each node, there is an eye or dormant bud comparable with that in a potato. Some eight to fifteen months are needed for the plant to reach maturity. Flowering takes place at a time of the year which varies with the country, but large numbers of canes never flower, and those that do rarely produce fertile seeds, so that the crop has been propagated from cuttings for generations.

A cutting is taken from the upper end of the stalk and of such length that it contains three nodes with attendant eyes. These cuttings are placed end-to-end in shallow furrows in rows from two to six feet apart, planting taking place at any time of the year when soil and climatic conditions are most favourable for growth. The eyes sprout within a few days and a single leaf emerges to produce a new cane which casts its leaves as it grows in length.

The crop needs very fertile soil, generous fertilising and frequent irrigation. On most of the world's plantations the practice is still to cut by hand, close to the ground, but in the sugar areas of Australia and the United States mechanical harvesters are used. After the cane is cut, the top is lopped off and it is then left in rows to be picked up later on for transportation to the factory for crushing. This must take place within forty-eight hours of cutting or there is a loss of sugar recovery. Plantations may be cropped for ten to fifteen years on good land and a good yield of sugar is half a ton per acre.

After crushing and extraction the residue is known as bagasse and is used to-day in the manufacture of wallboards, plastics and paper, and also in oil refining. The other by-product of the industry, molasses, is used for cattle feeding and the production of an endless list of chemicals.

Equally wide in its range of uses for the benefit of mankind is that tribe of fast-growing and often timber-sized grasses, the bamboos (*Bambuseae*). Native species are known in every continent except Europe, mostly in tropical and sub-tropical regions, although some hardy species grow in the temperate zone. Some six to seven hundred varieties are now classified into about sixty genera. Some grow to forest trees, others are slender and small. Some die at the end of a few years, others live for forty or more. Some shed their leaves like deciduous trees but bamboos which are native to river banks and the shade of tropical forests are generally evergreen. For a plant making such rapid growth—at Kew a culm of *Bambusa arundinacea* grew about 36 inches (91 cm.) in twenty-four hours—a rich, deep, loamy soil is required and a warm climate, although some species survive at temperatures below freezing point. Thus bamboos are found on the snow line of the Andes, 15,000 feet above sea level, and at 10,000 feet or more in the Himalayas. Some flower each year, others every few years, while some have never been known to flower and, owing to this infrequency of seed production, information concerning the growth and development of many members of the tribe is confined to vegetative shoots. The bamboos have hollow, jointed, glossy stems varying in colour from green to pale gold, although one variety has black stems, and others are spotted with brown or ringed with purple. Wonderful legends surround most of these unusually coloured specimens. The plant is rhizomatous and the roots have great penetrating powers, ramifying with great complexity both below and above the soil. In old bamboo clumps, it is not uncommon to find that the young rhizomes, unable to penetrate the mass of rhizomes below the surface, have doubled back on themselves until they reach a height of several feet. When the plant reaches full height it puts out branches at its upper nodes which are always two-ranked and alternate, like leaves.

The beauty of the bamboo has inspired artists and poets throughout the Far East, while more and more members of the tribe are appearing in western gardens and adding an intriguing tropical touch to some of our seaside resorts.

The uses of the bamboo are infinite. It was concerned with the beginnings of mathematics, for the earliest form of arithmetic consisted of calculating by means of bamboo billets; musical instruments, building, paper, food, kitchen utensils, farming and fishing gear, boats and bridges, barricades and weapons are but a few of the uses to which bamboos have been put. To-day, they have the same importance in the Orient as in ancient times; indeed, it is likely that the future will see increasing use and development of these truly remarkable grasses.

This chapter would not be complete without mention of certain other less important uses to which grasses have been put. Several species growing naturally on sand-dunes (for example, the marram grass) have been extensively used for controlling dune development on unstable coasts, and *Spartina* × *townsendii*, a natural hybrid between *S. alterniflora* and *S. maritima* which arose in Southampton Water, has been similarly used for the stabilisation of coastal mud flats.

Although grasses, apart from lawn grasses, are not usually thought of as garden plants, a number of species are strikingly handsome and are grown for ornament. Besides the bamboos, already mentioned, pampas grass (*Cortaderia* spp. from S. America), makes a fine clump with its feathery panicles, and several other smaller species can be effectively worked in to a herbaceous border, or naturalised in a wild garden, especially forms with variegated leaves (see the *R.H.S. Dictionary of Gardening* for a list of species).

Lastly, a number of grasses are scented and some are used as a source of perfume. Our own sweet vernal grass is delicately scented and the coumarin which it contains is partly responsible for the fragrance of new-mown hay. Holy grass (*Hierochloë odorata*) which grows in this country only in Caithness, Kirkcudbright, and Renfrew, and in Ireland, has a strong vanilla scent, also due to coumarin. In America it is said to induce sleep when hung in bundles over one's bed. The Indians make it into scented baskets, while it was used, in days gone by, both in Germany and Scandinavia, to strew in front of church doors—hence its name, holy grass.

In this country scented grasses have no economic importance, but in India and Ceylon a number of perfumed oils are produced. Lemongrass oil, citronella and palmarosa oil are well known and are used for keeping insects at bay. The grass from which lemon-grass oil is produced, *Cymbopogon citratus*, can also be infused to make lemon-grass tea which, it is recorded, was a favourite beverage of Queen Charlotte, the plant being supplied from the Royal Gardens at Kew for this specific purpose. How all-embracing and fascinating are the uses to which members of this family, Gramineae, can be put for man's benefit!

CHAPTER 18

LAWNS AND PLAYING FIELDS

The green turf of England has for centuries provided Englishmen with relaxation. This may be the simple relaxation found in a deck chair in a small suburban garden or more formal entertainment on the spacious lawns of one of our historic ancestral homes. Turf helps provide the excitements of race courses, the fun of pleasure grounds and the drama of ball games. A good turf has to satisfy many exacting requirements. It must be well-knit, durable and verdant under a wide range of conditions. It must play "true" for such exacting games as bowls, cricket and lawn tennis; it must withstand the hard wear of football boots, of pounding hooves or, as in our city parks, the treading of countless feet.

The following is a list of the most important grasses suitable for providing a good sward for the requirements of sport over a wide range of soils and conditions:

Agrostis tenuis (browntop)
Cynosurus cristatus (crested dogstail)
Festuca rubra subsp. *rubra* (creeping red fescue)
F. rubra subsp. *commutata* (Chewing's fescue)
F. tenuifolia (fine-leaved fescue)
Lolium perenne (perennial ryegrass)
Phleum pratense (timothy)
Poa nemoralis (wood meadow grass)
P. pratensis (smooth-stalked meadow grass)
P. trivialis (rough-stalked meadow grass)

It used to be common practice to include anything up to twelve species when composing a mixture for lawns but this has been proved by experiment and practical experience to be quite unnecessary and much smaller selections are now used. To quote a classical example,

here is a mixture prescribed in 1881 for the purpose of making a lawn
under shady conditions:

Alopecurus pratensis	1 lb. per acre
Anthoxanthum odoratum	1
Dactylis glomerata	3
Festuca duriuscula	3
Festuca ovina	1
Festuca pratensis	4
Lolium italicum	6
Lolium perenne	8
Phleum pratense	1
Poa nemoralis	2
Poa trivialis	2
Trisetum flavescens	1
Lotus corniculatus	1
Lotus major	1
Trifolium hybridum	3
Trifolium pratense	2
Trifolium pratense perenne	2
Trifolium repens	5
	—
	47

whereas for the same purpose and conditions to-day one would
prescribe:

Crested dogstail	20 per cent
Rough-stalked meadow grass	40
Wood meadow grass	40

Sown at the rate of 1-2 oz. per sq. yd.

The greater knowledge concerning the nutrition of the grass plant
and the advanced equipment for preparing the seed bed which are now
available, enable a greater precision to be achieved. Tilth and soil
nutrients receive the attention they merit and the seeds mixture is
selected for specific conditions and the purpose for which the turf is
required. Our forebears played for safety by including a large number
of species in the hope that at least some of them would survive.

For temperate climates, the best lawn grasses are found in the
genera *Agrostis* and *Festuca*, both providing species that are dwarf in
habit, firm in leaf, and persistent, withstanding regular hard cutting

by the mowing machine. Of the two, *Agrostis* is the more aggressive and enduring.

Of the *Agrostis* species, *A. tenuis*, commonly known as "browntop" is probably the most important. It spreads by means of short over-ground runners and from underground rhizomes and soon produces a thick carpet of grass. It is particularly suitable for impoverished soils. Under rich, moist conditions it tends to become somewhat aggressive when sown in conjunction with species of fescue which is the common practice. Although a common British grass, seed is not produced commercially in the British Isles, but is grown in New Zealand, harvested with a high purity and germination rate and exported as "New Zealand browntop." During recent years seed has also been imported from Oregon, U.S.A. The name "Chewings fescue " commemorates a certain Mr. Chewings who first selected and produced a crop of this important ingredient of grass mixtures about 1835. Like browntop, it is grown in favourable conditions in New Zealand, and is imported from there and also from Oregon. It is the best known of the red fescues, and is non-rhizomatous.

Under normal conditions, on a well-drained soil, a popular seeds mixture is one composed of:

Chewings fescue	70 per cent
New Zealand browntop	30

Under heavier, moisture-retentive soils, where the *Agrostis* tends to become aggressive, the mixture is generally modified to consist of:

Chewings fescue	90 per cent
New Zealand browntop	10

These two mixtures are suitable for bowling greens, but can, with certain additional grasses, form the basis for swards for other sports requirements. The introduction of crested dogstail into the mixture provides the hard-wearing, drought-resistant qualities required by cricket squares and tennis courts, and for these purposes the mixture then becomes:

Chewings fescue	75 per cent
New Zealand browntop	10
Crested dogstail	15

When, however, one wishes to establish a general-purpose lawn of fine texture the following mixture is suitable for a wide range of soils:

Chewings fescue	40 per cent
Creeping red fescue	30
Fine-leaved fescue	10
New Zealand browntop	20

In shady situations the inclusion of wood meadow grass and rough-stalked meadow grass is advisable since these grasses do especially well under such conditions.

Football pitches have to withstand very harsh treatment during the winter months and need grasses capable of standing up to such severe conditions and able to recover rapidly. A suitable mixture would be:

Perennial ryegrass	60 per cent
Crested dogstail	10
Creeping red fescue	10
Smooth-stalked meadow grass	10
Timothy	10

The problems of the golf course turn mainly on the fact that the game is played all the year round, and ideally the greens should be uniformly smooth and very fine, composed of a dense, close herbage providing a true playing surface for twelve months of the year. Fortunately, many courses are situated on soil formations of inherently low fertility and under these conditions the grasses will be stunted and dwarf in growth, giving a matted, springy turf which is ideal for the purpose. The actual greens are frequently composed of a wide variety of species, not all of them hard-wearing, but whereas in cricket or football no latitude is permissible in the layout of the pitch and the same areas must always take the really hard wear, in golf the position of the pin, where most of the wear occurs, can, within limits, be varied as occasion demands.

When a new lawn is to be established too much importance cannot be attached to the thorough preparation of the seed bed if the desired result is to be obtained. Lawns, be they sports fields or domestic, are normally put down as a permanent feature and thoroughness of procedure is likely to be more than justified. If the soil is very light in texture and overlies gravel the question of drainage is not likely to arise, but such soils are generally low in plant nutrients, and the fertility, therefore, must be improved before seeding takes place. Leaching of soil nutrients, common on such soils, can be slowed down by the addition of peat or well-rotted compost to the top soil during preparation. Should any grading be necessary, it is of the utmost importance that at least six inches of topsoil be left. This may involve the complete removal of the top soil, to be replaced after grading the subsoil.

In dealing with heavier soils, artificial drainage may be necessary. Proper drainage is absolutely essential, for this ensures good aeration, a more even distribution of plant nutrients, an improvement of soil texture, and better circulation of soil moisture. Well-drained soils, too, are warmer and growth commences earlier in the season and continues later in the autumn since growth is determined by soil temperature.

In sports fields and lawns where quick drainage is necessary the drains should be shallower than is common in agricultural practice. As a general rule the heavier the soil the nearer the drains should be to the surface and on really heavy ground a depth of 2 ft. 6 ins. at the lower or outlet end, allowing a fall of up to one foot in 100, ensures quick drainage. On medium soils, the drains may be as deep as 3 ft. at the outlet end. Distance apart varies from 10 ft. in heavy soils to 25 ft. in medium soils.

Cultivation is generally carried out during the summer for early autumn sowing on light soils or during the early winter for spring sowing on heavy soils. Wherever practicable, autumn sowing is generally to be preferred, for the soil temperature being high, quick germination follows and the young grass seedlings benefit from the morning dews. Every effort should be made to get the seedlings well established before the onset of frost and this will determine the latest date for safe sowing in any particular district.

It is seldom possible, however, to get a sufficiently fine tilth on heavy soils for autumn sowing and a much better course of action is to dig during the early part of the winter, leaving in the "rough"; frost then breaks down the clods in readiness for forking prior to sowing in the spring. Should the soil prove to be acid on testing, ground limestone should be applied at the rate of 2 to 4 oz. per square yard after the initial digging. The lime should never be dug in but maintained in the surface soil where the seedlings require it.

Weed seeds present in the soil should be encouraged to germinate during the fallow period prior to autumn sowing. These can readily be hoed and raked off before sowing is carried out. Annual weeds such as groundsel, chickweed and shepherd's purse compete strongly for moisture, food and space. When they appear in newly germinated grass, as sometimes happens, they should not be allowed to flower and seed, but should be removed by hand.

When the ground being prepared for a lawn is already covered with old turf this must be well buried or some of the old plants will survive, become re-established and will then contaminate the new sward. A good clear trench should be dug and maintained throughout the digging. The old turf should be pared off and placed upside-down in this trench, spit by spit. Provided sufficient depth of soil is placed above it, it will rot away, thereby improving the texture of the soil and aiding drainage at the same time. Couch grass—that unwanted invader of most gardens in temperate climates—can be disposed of in this manner if buried to a depth of at least one foot. Dandelions, docks and other perennial weeds should be removed by hand during digging; ground elder, devastating as this may be in the flower garden, can be ignored as it is readily killed by mowing.

Consolidation before sowing soon reveals the soft spots and these should be firmed and levelled off before a suitable fertiliser is applied. The level having been obtained, the following mixture may be applied at the rate of 3 oz. per sq. yd.:

Sulphate of ammonia	1	parts by weight
Superphosphate	2	
Bone meal	2	
Sulphate of potash	1	

This should be raked in seven to ten days before sowing, preferably using a wooden rather than an iron rake. The wooden rake should also be used for covering the grass seed.

After applying the fertiliser and before sowing the seed a fine tilth must be worked up by raking and cross raking. For high-grade lawns, the seed is sown at the rate of 1-2 oz. per sq. yd. When sowing by hand use marked-out yard strips; if a seed drill is used the setting should allow for sowing and cross sowing to avoid overlapping and gaps. Finally cover by raking and cross raking, making sure the seeding is carried out when the soil is dry. Rolling is unnecessary at this stage, but a light roller can be used with advantage when the seedlings are about one inch high.

The initial cut should be done when growth has reached about two inches high both for early autumn and spring sown swards. Cutting should, however, be in the form of topping only, the machine blades being set to leave an inch of grass. It is a good plan to give a light rolling a day or two before cutting to firm the seedlings in the soil and still allow time for the young grass to "upright" itself before cutting; thereafter the frequency and intensity of the mowing should be gradually increased. Heavy mowing must be avoided until the lawn has become well established.

Cricket squares, bowling greens, and other relatively small playing areas are more usually formed by turfing. This is much more expensive, but quicker in providing the final result. Even so, although turf gives an immediate grass cover, much care and attention is required before it can be accepted as a playing area of high quality. For instance weed species are invariably present and these need eradication as time goes on. The use of imported turf obviously precludes the measure of control over the species present which is possible when a prescribed mixture of grasses is actually sown. The standard-sized turf used for bowling greens is twelve inches square. The turves are cut accurately and are of uniform thickness. Turf used for other purposes is generally cut three feet by one foot, delivered in rolls to prevent damage and for ease of transport.

The superbly fine and smooth turf of many bowling greens has been established by turfing with "sea-washed turf," of which the best known is "Cumberland turf" though equally suitable material comes from coastal areas far removed from Cumberland. The chief species present is creeping red fescue, which, when well managed, produces a playing surface of unsurpassed excellence. Such turf, however, when replanted in an alien environment, frequently deteriorates, due to the ingress of coarse grass species such as annual meadow grass, and the development of the weed seeds already in the turf, such as sea-pink (*Armeria maritima*) sea-milkwort (*Glaux maritima*) and buck-horn's plantain (*Plantago coronopus*).

Thorough preparation of the ground is just as necessary for turfing as for seeding. Provided the turfs are laid on a perfectly levelled bed the highest degree of perfection will be obtained in the shortest possible time.

Turfing is an autumn or winter job. Spring droughts must be expected to delay the establishment of the sward and may cause drying out along the seams. It is beneficial, and indeed necessary when laying bowling greens, to bond the turfs. Top dressing should follow, using a sandy compost, the dressing being worked into the seams.

The establishment of lawns by vegetative means is costly and certainly more cumbersome than seeding. The grasses used in temperate regions are chiefly indigenous strains of *Agrostis stolonifera* var. *maritima* and to a lesser degree *Agrostis canina*. They are encouraged to produce their stolons in nurseries, and during August and September these stolons are removed from the parent plant, chopped into two-inch lengths, strewn on the bed which should be prepared as if seed were being sown and then covered with a light top dressing of soil. A light rolling and watering completes the operation. Shoots and roots will develop from each node and ultimately the whole area will be covered and a turf formed.

The cutting of lawns should be done according to the needs of the turf, and not by the day of the week or by the calendar! Lawn grass should never be allowed to get out of hand; this may even mean "topping" during mild spells during the winter. The height of the cut should be varied according to the season and to the conditions prevailing at the time. During dry spells the blades should be raised and the machine used without a box, allowing the cut grass to remain and act as a mulch. Rather more growth should be left in the autumn. More frequent mowings, with the machine set slightly higher, are more beneficial to the grass than less frequent and heavier cuts.

Many lawns are maintained in good condition for long periods without feeding, but there are many that would benefit from applications of plant nutrients. Grass requires a large number of mineral elements from the soil, especially nitrogen, phosphorous, and potassium. A deficiency of any one of these invites trouble, especially a shortage of nitrogen. Organic fertilisers such as dried blood, hoof and horn, fish meal and similar substances are useful but they must be used with thought and a measure of caution since they tend to encourage a soft, weedy and worm-infested turf. From practical experience it has been found that the most suitable quick-acting fertiliser is sulphate of ammonia applied at the rate of $\frac{1}{2}$ oz per. sq. yd; superphosphate applied at 1 oz. per sq. yd. will meet the phosphate requirements, while sulphate of potash supplies potassium and an application of $\frac{1}{4}$ oz. per sq. yd. is sufficient. A mixture of these three fertilisers does not keep well, so only the correct amount needed to cover the area to be dressed should be mixed, adding a carrier of screened soil and/or sand to facilitate even distribution. Excessive application of fertiliser is to be avoided, the aim being to produce density of turf rather than lushness which leads to fungus attacks and other troubles.

Fertilisers are best applied following rain or irrigation. Damage by scorching may follow application under very dry conditions.

Over-acidity is comparatively rare in garden lawns, the better lawn grasses preferring slightly acid conditions. Over-liming encourages earthworms and weeds. If lime is needed, as proved by soil analysis, it should be given in the form of ground limestone or ground chalk, in preference to quicklime or hydrated lime, and applied in autumn or winter at a rate of 2 to 4 oz. per sq. yd. according to the degree of acidity.

Newly sown lawns benefit from a top dressing given three or four months after sowing. This should be applied at the rate of 3 to 4 lb. per sq. yd. and should consist of finely prepared compost; it should be worked into the young grass by lightly brushing or raking, care being taken not to uproot young plants by being too heavy-handed.

The top dressing of established lawns should be a regular feature of their maintenance, the benefits derived from such treatment more than offsetting the trouble taken in preparing the compost. Farmyard manure, if obtainable, stacked in layers four to six inches thick, with layers of loam soil, six to nine inches, alternating, left for a twelve-month period and turned occasionally, provides a good dressing for this purpose. It should be screened through a fine riddle before mixing with sufficient sand or other sharp material to keep it friable, light and porous. Difficulty of obtaining suitable manure may make it necessary to use other organic materials such as composted vegetation, including lawn mowings, leaf mould, granulated peat, dried sewage and so on. Do not apply more thickly than the sward will absorb; it is far better to give two or three partial dressings of 3 to 4 lbs. per sq. yd. than one that simply swamps the mown grass. Top dressing should be carried out early in the season, say in February or March, depending on weather conditions at the time.

DISEASES

Fusarium patch or snow mould (*Griphosphaeria nivale*) appears as small yellowish patches which gradually increase in size. Eventually they may join up so that large areas are killed out. At the first sign of this disease curative measures must be adopted.

The trouble generally occurs during warm damp weather in late summer, autumn and occasionally in spring, and prevention is very much better than cure. Fungi, like all organisms of delicate structure, are very dependent on favourable environmental conditions. Such conditions are present when there is heavy dew, especially when there is little movement of air, as for example in areas closed in by buildings and trees. Heavy applications of fertilisers, especially nitrogen, can also create favourable conditions for attacks by fungi.

Efforts should be made to keep the grass as dry as possible by switching off the dew, using a long bamboo or similar switch, thereby allowing as much air movement as possible over the turf. Dressings of nitrogen fertiliser during late summer and autumn must be avoided.

There are several reliable proprietary turf fungicides on the market. These should be applied according to the manufacturers' instructions. One that is both dependable and inexpensive consists of a compound of malachite green and Bordeaux mixture. Others contain calomel and organic mercury compounds; the latter, of course, is poisonous and should be used with care.

Another common disease is *Corticium fuciforme* which appears during the summer and persists into the autumn. It attacks fescues primarily but also affects other grasses, which take on a bleached look, with small pink, branched needles of the fungus developing on the blades and sheaths. Patches of grass so affected are not killed but become seriously damaged and consequently unsightly. In serious cases treatment with a malachite green-Bordeaux mixture should be given. In less severe attacks, a light dressing of a nitrogenous fertiliser is often beneficial.

The presence of moss in lawns can be due to a number of factors such as infertility, over-acidity, very wet conditions due to poor drainage and rainy weather, or too severe mowing, to name but a few.

Moss produces abundant spores, but also spreads by vegetative means. The commonest species found in lawns are *Hypnum cupressiforme* and *Ceratodon purpureus*. *Polytrichum commune* is common on very poor soils. Control of moss means in the first place the correction of the cause of its presence. If a dense sward has been maintained there is little likelihood of an infestation, but if moss has become established, corrective treatment should be carried out. Lawn sand composed of a mixture of:

Sulphate of ammonia	3 parts
Calcined sulphate of iron	1
Dry sand, used as a carrier	20

can be applied at the rate of 4 to 6 oz. per sq. yd. This blackens and kills the moss, which can then be lightly raked out. Treatment is best done during dry weather, and should be repeated if necessary. Sulphate of iron may be used with good results when applied at $\frac{1}{2}$ oz. per sq. yd. either in solution or with sand as a carrier. Most proprietary moss killers include some compound of mercury such as calomel or corrosive sublimate. Following such treatment every effort must be made to build up the fertility by topdressing. Some re-seeding may also be necessary.

CHAPTER 19

SUMMING UP

Quite spectacular improvements have been effected in the realm of grassland husbandry in the past few decades. The impetus to increased food production demanded by war-time conditions in 1939-45, and the general improvement in standards of living experienced since the war, have focused attention on milk and meat production in particular. The pattern of improvement, however, is most uneven and the F.A.O. Report on the State of Food and Agriculture, 1959, indicates that the world situation is far from satisfactory. The increase in population outstrips the expansion in production by a large margin. In economically developed countries where the technical knowledge is advanced, the rate of improvement is accelerating, but in the less-developed countries there is a very marked lack of impetus towards improvement. There is no room for complacency in our own country, as we have already seen, for the production of a very large acreage of our grassland is well below maximum capacity. There is in fact, vast scope for expansion and development to bring the below-average farms to the standard of the best, and the output of our poor grassland to the level secured by the leading milk and meat producers of the country.

So far as the under-developed countries are concerned the chief cause of malnutrition is known to be a lack of the protective foods, especially those rich in protein and of animal origin. It has been estimated that if the world's diet is to reach a satisfactory level by the end of the present century, a three-fold increase in the output of animal products must be achieved. In those countries where the population rise is well above average and nutritional deficiencies are most serious, an even greater increase in the production of the essential foods is necessary.

Grassland in all countries will need to be exploited to the full, for much of the additional protein so essential for health must come from grazing animals in the form of meat, milk, butter and cheese. Five global pastoral systems have been postulated, based on the number of cattle units carried for every 100 acres of grassland. At one end of the scale, where the grassland management is on "very intensive" lines, pasture carries 80 cattle per 100 acres and the average yield per cow is around 860 gallons. At the other end of the scale, on a "very extensive" system, only 5 cattle units per 100 acres are carried and the average milk yield per cow is in the region of 42 gallons From this calculation the outstanding fact arises that some 5,000 million acres, or 86·4 per cent of the world's grassland, carries under 20 cattle units per 100 acres. The scope for development is clearly immense. It is estimated, moreover, that while half the world's total livestock are maintained in the region extending from 30° north of the equator to 30° south, the wide variations in stock-carrying capacity to be found in the various countries are due to nutritional factors rather than climatic or genetic ones. Put quite simply, lack of food is the limiting factor which prevents a vast expansion in livestock numbers without which a large part of the world's population will continue to starve.

The various stages in the reclamation of both forest lands and wide expanses of prairies and open country, towards more productive units of grass, have already been outlined in detail, but it is worthwhile broadening our canvas to allow a more simple picture to be drawn, encompassing the under-developed countries. There comes a time when nomads, tending their migratory herds and flocks, settle down. Homesteads are built and land enclosure is undertaken. These are extensive ranches at first, but in the course of time smaller units are found to be more productive than ranches and so fields with permanent fences are created on the pattern so familiar in this country. The whole business of building up fertility can now commence in earnest, for the dung and urine of the livestock is concentrated on a smaller area of land and better herbage plants can then be supported. Experience soon indicates that natural fertility can be enhanced by artificial means to increase the stock-carrying capacity. The plough is next introduced, and mixed farming begins, demanding higher standards of cultivation and management, the systematic use of fertilisers and seeds of high quality. At first this takes place near to the villages, but the villages soon grow into towns offering market facilities. As the towns grow, so transport facilities improve and the practice of good husbandry can spread further and further afield into the open country.

The introduction of better pasture plants and the use of fertilisers means that herbage can be conserved for winter fodder and no longer need the grazing policy and livestock numbers be regulated solely by the grazing season. Large numbers of livestock can be carried throughout the year and milk and meat production can proceed with nearly the same facility in winter as they do during the summer grazing period. More herbage per acre means more livestock per acre and this involves the control of animal disease and breed improvement. Advisory services are essential for such vast schemes of development, but unfortunately at the moment the supply of trained agriculturists is very far from adequate to cope with the gigantic task which confronts them. In backward areas little enough is known about livestock improvement and the knowledge concerning grassland husbandry is virtually non-existent. Moreover, the far-reaching social and political changes and general economic development in which the emerging nations are involved usually mean that agricultural improvement is far down the list of priorities. However, many men from under-developed areas are seeking training in this country, for the principles of sound agricultural practice are applicable the world over, even though specific local problems may be vastly different.

In chapter 13 we saw how the supply of water is a limiting factor in the growth of herbage plants. Environmental conditions for grass growth in the tropics are frequently very unfavourable. In the Middle East, north Africa, and north Australia the arid conditions under which pastures must grow inevitably mean that the plants are dessicated for a large part of the year. Plant breeders are seeking to produce strains which are drought-resistant, and some progress has been made in this direction. Even if they are successful, however, water in considerable quantities will be needed and the problem of ensuring that water supplies are both adequate and well distributed must be solved by engineers. If we in this country find the problem of meeting the needs of the livestock during the winter months a task requiring a good deal of ingenuity and the exercise of much skill and judgment, how much more acute must it be in the arid regions of the world!

It is in this connection that our experiences of "zero grazing," "mechanical grazing," or "soiling" are likely to prove so very helpful. Frequently, it is possible to grow a forage plant on a restricted scale under ideal conditions, and thus secure maximum growth when more normal cultivation is out of the question. The crop can then be cut and carted to the stock and fed in rationed amounts according to their needs. Striking results have been obtained from this system in Malaya, where elephant or Napier grass (*Pennisetum purpureum*) has been grown in rows on deeply cultivated and heavily fertilised and irrigated ground and the fodder cut and carted to the stock for feeding. Yields in the region of 100 tons of fresh grass per acre have been obtained in this way, while in this country Italian ryegrass grown under conditions of high fertility and irrigation has given spectacular yields in comparison with normal growth.

In the production and utilisation of grass a wide range of improved methods lies open to the British farmer and with the trend in the agricultural industry towards leaner times financially it is apparent that the grass plant must occupy an increasingly vital role in national planning and the business of farming. The tempo of research into grassland problems and animal health problems associated with grass feeding must speed up. Above all, the economic, social, political and, in some countries, even religious factors, which inhibit greater technical efficiency in grass farming, must be resolved. For too long grass has been a Cinderella amongst crops and only of recent years have men come to realise the tremendous contribution this crop can make to the health and productivity—and hence to the wealth and welfare—of any country.

BIBLIOGRAPHY

INDEX

BIBLIOGRAPHY

ARBER, A. (1934). *The Gramineae.* London.

BARNARD, C. S. (1958). Grassland and the Dairy Cow. *Westminster Bank Review*, May, 1958.

BEAUMONT, A. (1959). *Diseases of Farm Crops.* London.

BELL, G. D. H. (1948). *Cultivated Plants of the Farm.* London.

BEST, R.H. and COPPOCK, J.T. (1962). *The Changing Use of Land in Britain.* London.

BEYNON, V. H. (1957). Contribution of Grassland to the Economy of the Farm. *Agricultural Review*, August, 1957.
Grassland in England and Wales. *University of Bristol Report*, 106.

BOWDEN, W. M. (1959). The Taxonomy and Nomenclature of the Wheats, Barleys, and Ryes and their Wild Relations. *Canad. Journ. Bot.* 37: 657.

BRITISH WEED CONTROL COUNCIL (1965). *Weed Control Handbook.*

BROUGHAM, R. W. (1958). Interception of Light by the Foliage of Pure and Mixed Stands of Pasture Plant. *Aust. J. Agric. Res.* 1958: 9.

COOKE, G. W. (1960). *Fertilisers and Profitable Farming.* London.
(1964). The Basis of Modern Manuring. *Seale Hayne College Report.*

COPPOCK, J. R. (1964). *An Agricultural Atlas of England and Wales.* London.

DAVIES, W. (1960). *The Grass Crop.* London.

DAWSON R. B. (1949). *Practical Lawn Craft.* London.

ELLIOT, R. H. (1948). *The Clifton Park System of Farming.* London.

FRANKLIN, T. B. (1953). *British Grasslands.* London.

GILL, N. T. and VEAR, K. C. (1958). *Agricultural Botany.* London.

GILMOUR, J. S. L. and WALTERS, S. M. (1954). *Wild Flowers.* London.

GRASSLAND RESEARCH INSTITUTE (1961). *Experiments in Progress.* 1961: 13.

HALLIDAY, D. J. and TEMPLEMAN, W. G. (1951). Field Experiments in Selective Weed Control by Plant Regulators, Part IV. *Emp. J. of Expt. Agric.* 19: 104-12.

HOSKINS, W.G. and STAMP, L.D. (1963). *The Common Lands of England and Wales.* London.

HUBBARD, C. E. (1954). *Grasses.* Penguin.

IVINS, J. D. (Editor) (1959). *The Measurement of Grassland Productivity.* London.

JONES, M. (1933). Grassland Management and its Influence on the Sward. *Journ. R. Agric. Soc.* 94.

KENYON, K. (1960). Present Excavations at Jericho. *Advanc. Sci. Lond.* 17:

LOW, A. J. and ARMITAGE, E. R. (1959). Irrigation of Grassland. *Outlook on Agriculture* 2:5.

MANGELSDORF, P.C. (1947). The Origin and Evolution of Maize. *Advances in Genetics* 1:161.

MCCONNELL, P. (1962). *The Agricultural Notebook.* London.

MOORE, H. I. (1949). *The Science and Practice of Grassland Farming.* London.

(1950). *Grassland Husbandry.* London.

(1959). *Crops and Cropping.* London.

NATIONAL INSTITUTE OF AGRICULTURAL BOTANY. Cambridge Various Leaflets.

PAGE, J. W. (1939). *From Hunter to Husbandman.* London.

PAWSON, H. C. (1960). *Cockle Park Farm.* London.

REPORT OF THE COMMITTEE ON GRASSLAND UTILISATION (1958). *Cmnd.* 547. London.

ROLAND, A. (1881). *The Management of Grassland.* London.

SALISBURY, E. J. (1961). *Weeds and Aliens.* London.

SEMPLE, A. T. (1952). *Improving the World's Grasslands.* London, F.A.O.

SMITH, L.P. (1958). *Farming Weather.* London.

STAMP, L. D. (1946). *Britain's Structure and Scenery.* London.

(1955). *Man and the Land.* London.

STAPLEDON, R. G. (1935). *The Land: Now and To-morrow.* London.

TANSLEY, A. G. (1949). *Britain's Green Mantle.* London.

VOISIN, A. (1959). *Grass Productivity.* London.

WATSON, J. S. (1951). *Grassland and Grassland Products.* London.

WATSON, J. S. and NASH, M. J. (1960). *The Conservation of Grass and Forage Crops.* London.

WHYTE, R. O. (1960). *Crop Production and Environment.* London.

ZOHARY, D. (Hebrew University, Jerusalem) has published many papers on the origin and evolution of wheat and other cereals.

INDEX